LONDON'S RAILWAY HERITAGE

Architecture, Engineering and Industrial Archaeology

VOLUME THREE: NORTH (GER)

by Peter Kay

GER Lea Valley, Chingford, Enfield, Palace Gates, and Southbury Loop lines: Tottenham & Forest Gate Railway

CONTENTS

Silver Street in October 1935, after completion of the North Circular Road improvements including the new railway bridge in 1932. For more informatio see page 228.
D. J. Taylor collectio

NTRODUCTION & ACKNOWLEDGEMENTS

The highlight of this volume is the lengthy feature on the hitecture of the '1872' standard design stations on the monton (Enfield) and Walthamstow (Chingford) lines, which ve never been subjected to serious analysis previously. (This ludes Bethnal Green which was technically in Vol. 2). As in lume 2, a large number of photographs of *since demolished* ildings and structures have been included in order to give l context to those that remain; the captions always state ien a building no longer exists.

The viaducts featured in this volume, Bethnal Green - ckney Downs and the Tottenham & Forest Gate line, both ve much simpler histories than the earlier London & ckwall and Eastern Counties viaducts featured in the evious volumes; however their 'late' dates have led to them ing almost wholly neglected in print hitherto.

The Lea Valley line is covered as far as the Essex county undary only. The Southbury Loop has been dealt with in full, it would have been foolish to omit Theobalds Grove station d the northernmost portion of the line in Hertfordshire.

The line-order tabulations in this volume *include* most post-40s bridges, whereas in the early stages of this project, in the sex volumes, they were largely omitted altogether as lacking y 'heritage' interest.

All the station buildings on the Palace Gates branch and the &FG line, and almost all on the Lea Valley line, are long since molished, and in consequence they are not covered here. The a Valley line has a minimal number of older structures of *any* nd remaining.

The pre-1980s photographic content of this volume is almost tirely due to the views taken by, or photographs from the llections of, Jim Connor and Dave Taylor; neither the detailed search nor the publication of a properly illustrated book ould have been possible without them.

I am also grateful to Chris Pond, principal author of the 970 and 1975 books on the Chingford line (which were well in advance of their time in the coverage given to stations and infrastructure) for recent correspondence on the stations on that line. Also to Dave Cockle, Brian Pask, Alex Hamilton, and others.

This volume marks the end of the series, at least for the present. A further volume could readily be put together on the GN lines in North London (and the title of this volume has been chosen in case that comes to pass). However much of the rest of London would not be economically viable, as it would be necessary to start research from scratch on companies hitherto unexplored (and in the case of northwest London, several very large national companies, requiring the ploughing through of numerous records not principally London-centric at all). On top of which, there is nothing for other companies to compare to the great quantity of accessible material produced / accumulated over the years by the Great Eastern Railway Society, much of it now word-searchable at home, and a great encouragement to the viable production of works on minority-interest subjects.

Sadly, also, the sales of Volume 2 have proved significantly lower than those of Volume 1, when the expectation had been that, with a larger number of older photographs and a greater emphasis on station buildings, it would have been *more* popular than Volume 1. Obviously it was never expected that these specialist titles would secure *large* sales, but there must be a bottom line drawn! It has been a particular disappointment that so little interest has materialised from the 'London industrial archaeology' side, as it has always been the accepted wisdom that railway infrastructure was their number one field of interest. Again, it has unfortunately proved impossible to get through to the 'heritage' and 'architectural' markets.

Peter Kay, Wivenhoe

April 2015

13. THE LEA VALLEY LINE

(Stratford) to Essex county boundary north of Enfield Lock (GR 364000)

Opened 1840, Northern & Eastern Railway, later Great Eastern Railway

Very few old structures survive on this line, as there was a major station rationalisation exercise in 1970, and there were few bridges of substance.

BRIDGE 655, overbridge, Temple Mills Lane, GR 384854. 1964, concrete beams, three spans.

Temple Mills Yard staff cottages, Ruckholt Close (formerly Quarter Mile Lane). Terrace of six cottages, 1881 (contract to Atherton & Latta 3.5.1881 at £1,870). To a design not known elsewhere, with the end cottages having projecting gabled sections. Heavily modernised in recent years, with replacement windows. [Station Master's house built adjacent under same contract demolished].

Staff cottages, Leyton, Dunedin Road and Auckland Road. 25 cottages remain from 40 built in 1902/3 for the tenants of houses at Angel Place, Stratford demolished for the extension of Stratford Works (approved by Way & Works Committee 7.10.1902 at £13,775). Photos below.

Eurostar Depot, 2007.

BRIDGE 663, overbridge, Lea Bridge Road, GR 362871. Rebuilt 1959, two concrete beam spans. To the west is the remaining portion of the road viaduct constructed by the N&ER in 1840, segmental arches, stock brick. Photos p.187. The portion to the east of the line no longer exists.

LEA BRIDGE

Of the 1840 structures, only the lower parts of the brick stairs between the Booking Hall and the platforms remain. The station platforms also remain.

BRIDGE 664A, footbridge, 'Black Path', GR 359873. c.1930, red brick stairs, plate girder span with plate parapets.

BRIDGE 664B, underbridge, Flood Relief Channel, GR 356876. 1959, concrete beams, three spans.

BRIDGE 666, underbridge, originally East London Water Works aqueduct, now footpath, GR 354877. Passenger lines bridge 1962, welded steel girders, three spans. Goods lines bridge (disused) 1932, plate girder, transverse troughing, two spans.

[BRIDGE 667, see Chingford line Bridge 1888]

BRIDGE 1391, underbridge, Copper Mill stream, GR 350880. Two spans, one over road underpass (in connection with now-closed level crossing), the other over the stream. Road bridge reconstructed 1967, welded steel girders and longitudinal troughing, 5ft headroom. Passenger lines stream bridge 1894, plate girder, 30ft span. Goods lines stream bridge (disused) 1912, plate girder, 30ft span.

BRIDGE 1393, underbridge, River Lea, GR 345887. Passenger lines bridge 1896, plate girders, cross girders and joists (contract to Head Wrightson 7.7.1896 at £2,057). Goods lines bridge (disused) c.1911, same construction but upper parts removed. Both bridges 76ft 3in span (84ft 6in on skew). Photos p.188.

[BRIDGE 1394, see T&FG line Bridges 27-29].

BRIDGE 1395, overbridge, Ferry Lane, GR 345895. 1911, originally four plate girder spans each with six main girders, longitudinal concrete jack arching, and plate parapets; steel stanchion intermediate supports (except one brick pier). Main lines span rebuilt 1968 with concrete beams and brick parapet wall. Easternmost span now used by private road.

TOTTENHAM / TOTTENHAM HALE

Underground ticket hall building 1968. BR portion of station wholly rebuilt 1990/1.

Further Reading – *GE Journal* 122.

PARK / NORTHUMBERLAND PARK

Small flat roof Booking Office building 1970. Passenger footbridge: steel trestles 1929, new higher steel span 1968. Footbridge at level crossing concrete, 1960s.

ANGEL ROAD

[No station structures remain]. Footbridge steel, late C20.

PONDERS END

Small flat roof Booking Office building 1970. Footbridge concrete, 1968.

BRIMSDOWN

Station Master's house portion only remains of large 1884 main building (photos p.188). Small flat roof Booking Office building 1970.

ORDNANCE FACTORY / ENFIELD LOCK

Station Master's house 1891 (part of the new station buildings of that year, the rest demolished 1970 except for red brick wall behind down platform). Small flat roof Booking Office building 1970. Footbridge concrete, 1969.

Two of the cottages in the main terrace of fourteen in Dunedin Road remain unspoilt. These 1902/3 Leyton cottages are to the same exterior design as the 1899 cottages on the south side of Foster Road, Parkeston (photo *ERH* p.56) and the 1902 Ley Street cottages (*LRH* Vol.2 p.125). The doorway at left remains in original form, showing that these cottages had 'porch' entrances as per the Ley Street drawings.

General view of the 1902/3 terrace of six cottages o the north side of Dunedin Road west of Aucklan Road. Apart from the inevitable new windows, they ar little altered.

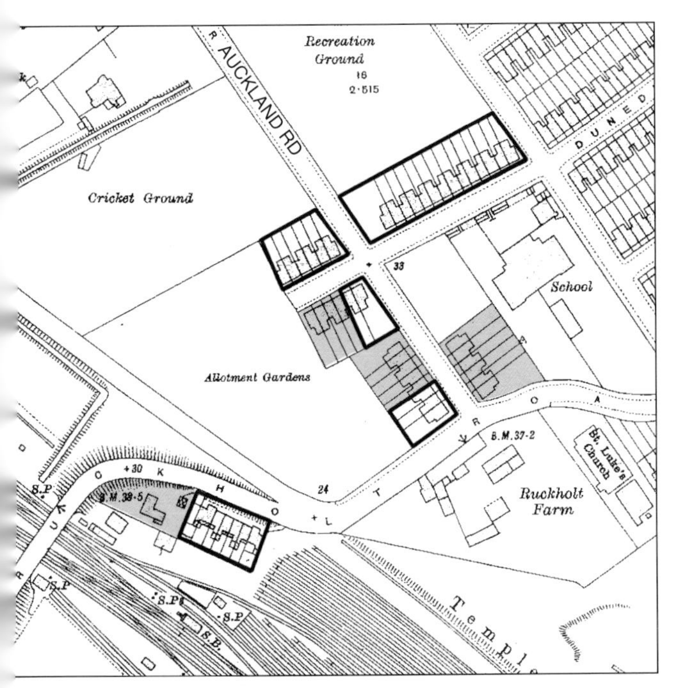

Left: 1914 OS showing the Ruckholt Road and Auckland Road / Dunedin Road GER cottages. Dark outlining indicates those still standing, light shading those now gone. Thirteen of the 1902/3 cottages were lost in the war; the two at the south end of Auckland Road (east side) followed when Ruckholt Road was diverted northwards. The Ruckholt Road SM's house lasted until demolished in recent years for a new slip road.

Below: The Lea Bridge Road viaduct, long since 'forgotten' as a railway work, was actually one of the major works on the first section of the Northern & Eastern Railway, and the provisions for it take up no less than six pages in the 1839 Act. The road had to be raised 18 feet, on a gradient of no more than 1 in 45. The roadway was required to be 55ft wide with a 10ft pavement either side.

On the 1895 OS 1:1056 map here, the viaduct was still wholly intact, but there had been one major change visually, insofar as the ground on the north side over the stretch A-D had been raised up to viaduct level, rendering the viaduct invisible on this side. In 1840 the only existing building in the vicinity was the Greyhound public house, and this had to be provided with a footbridge from the viaduct to a new entrance door at first floor level. Subsequently however a new pub building was erected as seen here, with a forecourt at viaduct level. The section D-E of the viaduct's north wall still exists and can be seen from this forecourt, but the arches are hidden by heavy alterations.

On the south side however the wall and arches are still visible over the section A-E. A roadway (now 'Lammas Road') runs alongside here at original ground level; it initially gave access to a non-public level crossing over the line leading to N&ER ground on the east side. (There had also been a temporary road here whilst the bridge was under construction – the viaduct is on the original road alignment).

To the east of the line, the south side wall originally ended at B and the north side wall at C, but nothing now remains at this end following the construction of Argall Way and Orient Way. The lowest sections at the far west and east ends did not of course have arching.

The majority of the arches were rebuilt in 1919/20. The plans of that date show 16 arches west of the line and 17 to the east.

LEA BRIDGE ROAD VIADUCT

›e photographs below, taken in 2014, show the remaining section of the ›a Bridge Road viaduct, west of the railway, south side of the road.

›*low left:* The highest portion, immediately west of the bridge, with the ›idue of the recently removed steps up to the bridge (not an 1840 feature ›t present by the 1860s OS). The railings are modern.

›*low right:* Taken from the same spot looking west along Lammas Road. ›e arches are now numbered 1-14 west to east.

›*ttom left:* From near the west end. It would appear that there must have ›en a further two arches behind the rendered section. On the westernmost ›rtion without arching, the (assumed) original large coping stones are still ›situ (left). The now-closed second Greyhound pub building looms above.

›*ttom right:* A closer view of 'arch 6'. The segmental arches have ›erpendicular' coursing. Everything is in stock brick, however the bricks ›ed in the piers have a more reddish hue. Most of the visible work must ›e 1919/20 rather than 1840.

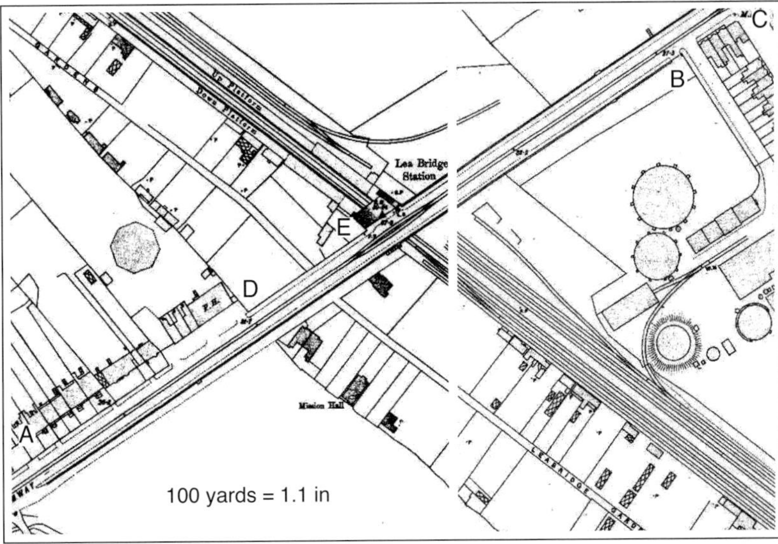

The N&ER 1839 Act required a 'sufficient railing and fence as shall be required by the said General Surveyor, at the outer edge of the footpaths'. The railings provided were the same as those on the contemporary London & Blackwall Railway viaduct (*LRH* Vol. 1 p.5). The link between the to was no doubt Bidder. These railings remained in part into the postwar years; the photograph shows the far west end of the viaduct, south side. All are now gone.

View under the River Lea passenger lines bridge (Bridge 1393).This bridge has a low clearance for river craft: the 1839 Act had specified minimum clearances, and in this 1896 replacement bridge the eight longitudinal joists are set low in the cross girders to improve clearance. The Goods lines bridge is seen at left.

The 1839 Act required 'a good and substantial Brick, Stone, or Cast Iron Bridge, of not more than Two Spans or Openings, with a clear Waterway of not less than Eighty Feet, and a Towing Path of not less than Eight Feet in width'. This was fulfilled – although the 1896 bridge is not of *cast* iron!

West side of the 1911 River Lea Goods lines bridge.

The 1911 Ferry Lane bridge at Tottenham Hale station, looking south.

The 1884 Brimsdown buildings are / were a somewhat odd thing, even allowing the general lack of consistency in GER station architecture on existing lines pr 1883 (it is likely that Brimsdown was *designed* just before Ashbee moved to GER). It is true that there are a *few* elements in common with the 1880 Bush Park main building. The road side of the surviving SM's house portion (above) loc more like a contemporary pub. The upper part of the platform side (below) is decid inelegant. Apart from the replacement windows, everything seems to be in origi condition. A bright red brick is used throughout, but there is too much dirt recognise this, except on the cleaned lower part on the platform side.

The red brick Station House at Enfield Lock, which retains its original windows.

4. THE 1847 ENFIELD BRANCH

(Angel Road) to Enfield Town

Opened 1847, Eastern Counties Railway, later Great Eastern Railway

Line closed and lifted from Angel Road Jn to Edmonton Jn

Current status of trackbed on closed section:

Angel Road Jn to Montagu Rd (GR 350927)	Rough ground / scrapyard
Montagu Road to Pleuna Rd (GR 345933)	Public footpath
Pleuna Road to Edmonton Jn	Eliminated except for short section alongside current railway on approach to junction

LOWER EDMONTON LOW LEVEL

[No remains]

BRIDGE 1961, underbridge, Salmons Brook, GR 432940 (adjacent to Bridge 1962). Two 15ft spans, joists and concrete jack arching.

BRIDGE 1963, footbridge, GR 342940. c.1900, Debden type (*ERH* p.49). Lifted 3ft 1957. 45ft span.

Edmonton Junction signal box base, ruinous. (McK&H Type 1 box of 1872).

BRIDGE 1964, overbridge, Bury Street, GR 341945. 1958 concrete beam span.

Bury Street Junction signal box base. (GER Type 8 box of 1891).

BRIDGE 1965, overbridge, First Avenue / Park Avenue, GR 337953. 1958 concrete beam span and parapet walls, old abutments.

BUSH HILL PARK

Up side buildings and platform canopy 1880, both extended at north end 1894 to accommodate an up side Booking Office. Alterations to openings and interior at north end for new B.O. arrangements 1982 after fire. Down platform single-storey flat-roof building c.1970, now taxi office. Steel footbridge 2010. [1880 main building and down platform canopy removed 1966].

Lincoln Road level crossing. Single manual gates.

ENFIELD TOWN

Main building, and canopy on island platform, 1957/8. (Photos p.190).

The 1880 Bush Hill Park canopies were of the standard type for the period, with 'quatrefoil' brackets and curved sawtooth valancing (*ERH* p.42). The capitals are similar to some of those at Bishops Stortford up side (*ERH* p.119 bottom right). *D.J. Taylor*

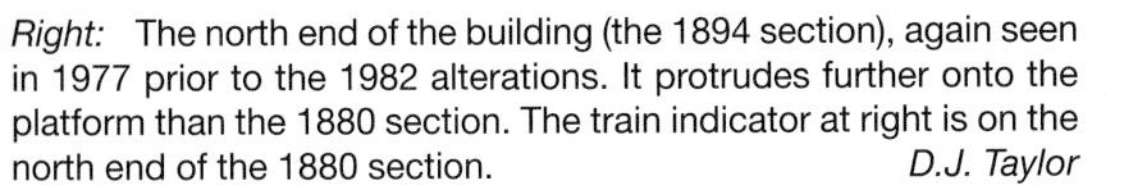

Right: The north end of the building (the 1894 section), again seen in 1977 prior to the 1982 alterations. It protrudes further onto the platform than the 1880 section. The train indicator at right is on the north end of the 1880 section. *D.J. Taylor*

When the up side building Bush Hill Park was built 1880 there was no entrance this side, hence the lack of a attempt at an architectu composition as seen from street. The 1894 extension the entrance / B.O. (to the ri of the chimney as seen he was in the same style. T details are as per the no gone main down side buildi The GER Engineer A Langley was responsib Photograph again 1977; m openings are now bricked u

D.J. Tay

Enfield received a seco station building in 1872, not the standard Metropolit Extensions style (because was not part of those work but in the charge of the GE Engineer Davis). However was decided to bui replacement structures for t electrification in 1957/8. At le in this August 1958 view is t 1872 Station Master's hous which survived initially but h now gone.

Included in the 1957/8 schem was a new concrete canopy fo the island platform, seen her in 1960, already lookin somewhat less than pristine.

5. THE CHINGFORD LINE

(Hackney Downs) to Chingford

Hackney Downs to Hall Farm Jn opened 1872, Hall Farm Jn to Shern Hall Street opened 1870, Shern Hall Street to Chingford Goods opened 1873, Chingford Goods to Chingford opened 1878. Great Eastern Railway.

CLAPTON TUNNEL No. 1 (Bridge 1378), 445 yards. 1871. The south end 'portal' is a plate girder bridge (Bridge 1377, Downs Park Road). North end mouth has horseshoe arch.

BRIDGE 1379, overbridge, Heyworth Road, GR 347859. 1957 concrete beam span, 1871 abutments.

BRIDGE 1380, overbridge, Charnock Road, GR 347860. 1957 concrete beam span, 1871 abutments.

BRIDGE 1381, overbridge, Ferron Road, GR 347861. 1957 concrete beam span, 1871 abutments.

CLAPTON TUNNEL No. 2 (Bridge 1382), 282 yards. 1871, horseshoe arch mouths, five rings.

BRIDGE 1383, overbridge, Clapton Road, GR 347865. Reconstructed 1958.

CLAPTON

B.O. building including covered stairs to up platform 1872, interior renovated 1985/6. Replacement covered footbridge fronting road 1958. Up platform building and canopy (6¾ bays) 1872, in original condition. Stairs to down platform 1979, steel. [Down platform canopy demolished 1970s]. Down platform Waiting Rooms block (north of Bridge 1384) 1881, and extension c.1900, both boarded up. (Photos pp. 232/234/237/241/243).

BRIDGE 1384, overbridge, Southwold Road, GR 347866. 1871, skew, plate girder, three spans 7ft 0in / 33ft 0in / 7ft 0in, with six cast iron columns on each platform carrying girders as intermediate supports. Cross girders and jack arching. Brick parapet walls. (Photo p.192).

BRIDGE 1385, overbridge, former Comberton Road (road now closed), GR 348867. Replacement bridge 1958, concrete beam span on new concrete abutments, red brick parapet walls.

BRIDGE 1386, overbridge, former Aveley Road (road now closed), GR 349868. Replacement bridge 1957, concrete beam span on new abutments, red brick parapet walls.

BRIDGE 1387, overbridge, Mount Pleasant Hill, GR 349868. 1957, Replacement bridge 1957, concrete beam span on new abutments, red brick parapet walls.

BRIDGE 1388, underbridge, Leaside Road (originally occupation), GR 351871. 1871, plate girder, two main girders, underslung cross girders, joists and plate decking. 40ft span. (See p.210).

BRIDGE 1389, underbridge, Lea Navigation, GR 351872. 1871, double Pratt truss (hogback), two main girders, cross girders, joists and plate decking, stock brick abutments, 85ft span. (Photos p.193).

Brick viaduct on either side of bridge, stock brick, 1871. To south one 35ft segmental arch (537) plus 12ft span semicircular arch over towpath (538). To north five 35ft segmental arches (540-544, *alias* 539-543). Note: these arch numbers follow on from those on the Enfield line.

BRIDGE 1887, underbridge, occupation, GR 353874. 1871, stock brick, two five-ring segmental arches each of 21ft span.

For the building of this line, see page 198.

For illustrations and further details of the Clapton / St James Street / Hoe Street / Wood Street station buildings, see the Feature on 1872 type stations.

The wholly-reconstructed Comberton Road overbridge, Clapton, seen on 6th March 1959 when still clean and new. The similarly-rebuilt Aveley Road bridge appears beyond. A very clean 69604 heads the 1.23pm from Chingford. *H.B. Priestley, courtesy MP 92 1/2*

BRIDGE 1888 (Lea Valley line Bridge 667), underbridge, occupation / Lea Valley line / footpath (formerly aqueduct), GR 354877. To west of Lea Valley line two 31ft segmental arches, 1872, stock brick. Remainder of bridge is replacement 5-span viaduct, 1960, welded steel girders on concrete piers (photo p.194), however both the abutments, and the southernmost intermediate pier, are of brick, from the previous structure. 8 main girders, cross girders and steel decking, plate parapets.

BRIDGE 1888A, underbridge, flood relief channel, GR 358853. 1955, welded steel girders.

BRIDGE 1889, underbridge, occupation road and former stream, GR 358853. c.1866, two brick arches each of 22ft span.

BRIDGE 1890, underbridge, Essex Road (originally occupation), GR 361885. c.1866, stock brick, three-ring segmental arch, brick parapet walls, 12ft 0in span.

BRIDGE 1891, underbridge, St James Street, GR 364887. 1901 (when road was widened), plate girder, three main girders and transverse troughing. 42ft 10in span.

ST JAMES STREET

Up platform u1870, down platform 1873, both on stock brick arching (segmental arches) throughout.

Booking Office 'building' (partly under line) east of St James Street 1870, altered 1901. (West wall 1901, north and south walls 1870 but most window / door openings 1901). The line passes above on girders (Bridge 1892: rebuilt 1901). Booking Hall interior 1974. Bases only of up and down platform buildings, u1870 / 1875. Platform 'shelters' 1974, altered c.1990. [Remaining 1870s platform buildings, canopies, and stairway coverings demolished 1974]. Stairways brick, the upper parts on both sides 1870/3, now uncovered, the middle parts including stairs from Booking Hall 1901, the narrow lower sections u1970s in same style. Shop on north side 1901, originally the exit lobby for down side stairs. (Photos p.221).

HOE STREET / WALTHAMSTOW CENTRAL

Main building on up side, and up platform canopy (six bays), 1870, in largely original condition. [Canopy was extended at west end 1907, this section demolished c.1967]. Photos pp. 219 / 220 / 244. Down platform canopy 1873, originally six bays but the westernmost two demolished c.1967. Booking Hall structure on down side 1968. [Footbridge removed 1976. Gents block on up platform now demolished].

BRIDGE 1897, overbridge, Hoe Street. GR 374890. Plate girder, widened on both sides c.1900, replacement 1957 concrete decking, 1901 engineering brick facing to abutments and parapet walling, 25ft span. Contiguous bridge added on east side 1931 to carry three shops (shops since removed). (Photo p.194).

BRIDGE 1898, overbridge, West Avenue, GR 375890. Replacement bridge 1958, concrete beam span on new abutments, red brick parapet walls. (Originally three-arch bridge: outer arches bricked up 1958).

Southwold Road Bridge 1384 from the north side, i.e. looking from the down platform to the up. The considerable skew of this bridge, evident from the angle between the north side main girder at top and the cross girders carrying the jack arching, necessitated the expensive construction. The are six columns on each platform carrying the intermediate support girders. This bridge and Bridge 1900 Vestry Road were the only two original overbridges on the line to survive electrification.

BRIDGE 1899, overbridge, East Avenue, GR 376891. Replacement bridge 1958, concrete beam span on new abutments, red brick parapet walls.

BRIDGE 1900, overbridge, Vestry Road, GR 378891. c.1866, stock brick, segmental arch (four rings), 25ft span. (Photo p.194).

BRIDGE 1901, Nag's Head Tunnel, 71 yards, GR 379891. Under Orford Road and to east thereof. c.1866, stock brick, cut and cover tunnel, horseshoe arch mouths (five rings with keystones). (Referred to as 'a short tunnel built as a covered way' in 1870 MT6). (Photo p.194).

BRIDGE 1902, overbridge, Shernhall Street, GR 382893. Replacement bridge 1958, concrete beam span on new abutments, red brick parapet walls.

BRIDGE 1903, underbridge, Wood Street, GR 385894. 1871, three main girders, underslung cross girders, joists and plate decking, 36ft span. (Photos p.210).

WOOD STREET

Platforms built on 1873 stock brick arching throughout. Booking Office building at road level 1974/5, flat roof. Platform 'shelters' 1974/5. Stock brick stairways 1873, now uncovered. [1873+ platform buildings and canopies, and stairway coverings, demolished 1974, except brick base of up platform building remains]. Photos pp. 225/242.

BRIDGE 1905, overbridge, Forest Road, GR 385901. Replacement bridge 1958, concrete beam span on new abutments, red brick parapet walls.

BRIDGE 1906, underbridge, Macdonald Road, GR 384904. 1873, stock brick, four-ring segmental arch, brick parapet walls, 21ft span. Widened on west side 1876.

BRIDGE 1907, underbridges, River Ching and footpath, GR 385914. River bridge is original 1873 semicircular arch (three rings), stock brick, 13ft span; widened on west side 1876. Footpath bridge c.1957, RSJs covered in concrete. 20ft span. (Photo p.194).

HALE END / HIGHAMS PARK

Main building on up side 1903 (contract to J. Parnell 6.10.1903 at £2,431). Booking Hall / Waiting Room interiors 1979. [Portion of building at north end demolished 1979]. Up platform canopy: five bays at south end 1903, two bays in middle 1958, five bays at north end c.1934. Store Room on up platform 1880s, brick, flat roof. Footbridge, concrete, 1957 (Frinton type, see *ERHS* p.109). Subway (Bridge 1908) at south end 1909, including stairway to / entrance from station forecourt. Down platform canopy c.1934, six bays. (Photos pp.195/196).

Signal Box, LNER Type 11a, jettied, 1925. Abolished 2002, restored by local group, now builder's office.

Further Reading: *London Railway Record* 76.

BRIDGE 1911, overbridge, Simmons Lane, GR 387936. 1957, concrete beam span on new abutments. 24ft 9in span.

BRIDGE 1912, underbridge, Kings Road, GR 388940. 1931, plate girder, cross girders and railbearers, cantilevered plate parapets. 50ft span.

BRIDGE 1912A, footbridge, GR 390943. 1920, original brick stairs, replacement steel span.

CHINGFORD

Main building on down side 1878, interiors 1979. Gents block by Platform 1 stops 1979. Platform canopies 1878 (both originally ten bays, canopy on Platforms 3/4 cut back by two bays at south end c.1970s).

[1878 Waiting Rooms behind Platform 3 demolished. 1910 up side Booking Office building demolished].

Four GER cottages (Nos 105/107/109/111 Beresford Road), date nk but 1890s, similar to the Debden cottages at *ERH* p.50 but the first floor windows are wider. All heavily altered.

Further Reading – *GE Journal* 107.

bove (montage): Bridge 1389 looking south east. The truss girders of this bridge are virtually identical to the 1880 ommercial Road (Limehouse curve) bridge illustrated at Vol. 1 p.35. In a *double* Pratt truss bridge each diagonal xtends across *two* bays. At left is Arch 540 *alias* 539, the first of the five arches on the north side of the river, which ne imagines were provided for flood relief purposes. These are in stock brick with five-ring segmental arches.

elow: A closer view of the bridge girders.

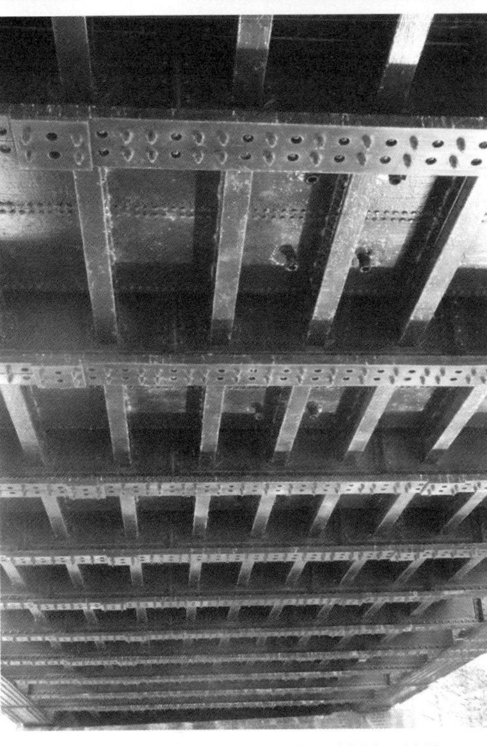

The cross girders joists and plate decking of Bridge 1389 are as per the 1871 three-span bridges 1351 and 1363 (p.211 bottom).

1866-73 BRICK ARCH UNDERBRIDGES

The underbridges on the section of the Walthamstow line built in 1865/6 and 1869/70 were to the standard Metropolitan lines design (as illustrated also by the Edmonton line examples at p.207).

Left: The brick arch portion of Bridge 1888 (built 1871). In these 1866-73 brick arch underbridges, there is a band of proud brickwork above the arch, which usually has the same number of courses as the number of rings in the arch (3, 4 or 5).

Right upper: Essex Road Bridge 1890 (built c.1866). This bridge was built for double track although only one line was laid initially.

Bottom left and right: Macdonald Road bridge was on the 1873 Chingford line but was built to the same design. It was, perhaps surprisingly, built for single track and widened for the 1876 doubling (right).

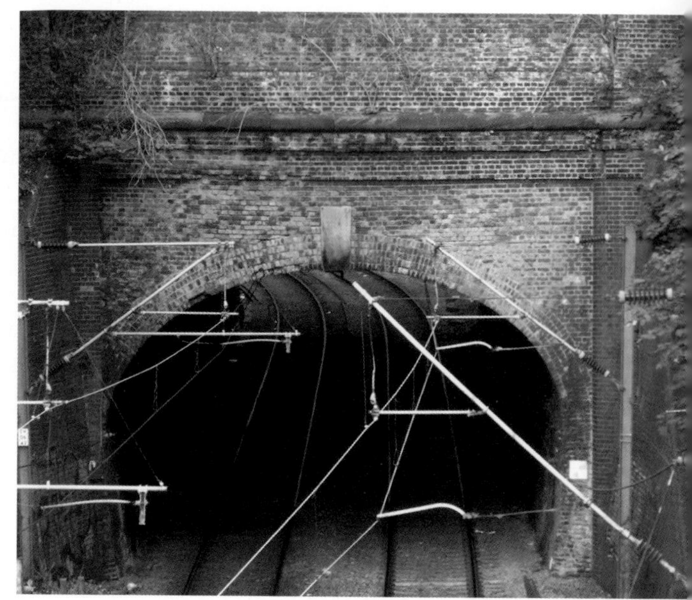

The ordinary brick arch overbridges were to the same design as the underbridges, the only survivor being Vestry Road (left).

Right: The cut-and-cover Nag's Head Tunnel, west end, horseshoe mouth with keystone. This tunnel did not have to be altered for electrification and remains in its original state today.

Bridge 1897 (Hoe Street) from the up platform. The c.1900 widened portion is several feet greater in span. It is unclear what if anything remains from the original bridge of c.1870.

Bridge 1907, photographed in 1909 after it achieved fame through its involvement in the 'Tottenham Outrage', when one of the eastern European revolutionaries shot himself here after failing to climb the fence between the Ching Brook and the footpath. This is the view east, with the original plate girder footpath span at left.

Right: The very modern main portion of Bridge 667/1888 (the GER always gave *two* numbers to bridges that carried one of its lines over another).

HIGHAMS PARK

ale End [Highams Park] and the
st Chingford station were given
ly 'temporary' wooden buildings
hen the line opened in 1873. When
e local population began to grow,
replacement building for Highams
ark was inevitable, and after some
etting over excessive costs the
ork was carried out in late 1903.
he single-storey building – a
etached station master's house
ad already been provided in 1891 –
as to a restrained design by
omparison with Ashbee's 1890s
ations Maryland to Ilford,
orrowing from them only the
esign of the large window in the
ooking Hall. It was also
onstructed in a pale cream brick,
ave for the red brick of the bottom
n courses and the window
ressings. Ashbee clearly had a
enchant for this cream brick in
903 as the cottages at Ingatestone
RH p.52) also date from that year.
This building still exists in original
xterior condition, save that the
ain entrance doorway was
onverted to another window in the
960s (?) and the roadside canopy
emoved. Also the chimneys
sappeared in the major exterior
efurbishment carried out in 1979.

Andrew Golds collection

he up platform canopy in its post-
958 state (photographed in 1969).
he original 1903 canopy at the
outh end (right) was of five bays
nly (six columns). In the c.1934
nprovements a separate section of
ve bays / six columns (left) was
onstructed north of the original
ootbridge, with plain steel I-section
olumns and a unique (?) style of
arge three-circle brackets, but with
he valancing made to the GER
tandard design to match the
riginal portion. Finally in 1958 when
he original footbridge was removed
n infill section of two bays (one
ew column in 1930s style) was
erected in the middle, and this too
was given 'standard' valancing. The
non-standard spacing of the
columns at this point will be noticed.

Jim Connor collection

The entirely new down platform canopy of c.1934 (right) used second-hand columns of the elaborate mid-1880s type originally featured at Coborn Road (1883), Globe Road (1884), March (1885) and Braintree (1886). Out of these stations the only likely source for surplus columns was Globe Road, where the canopies seem to have been dismantled prior to this. The brackets however are of the same 'three circles' type as used in the c.1934 portion of the up canopy. Again, 'standard' valancing was provided to match. The southernmost bay has been removed since this 1968 photograph.

J.E. Connor

Far left and left: Column and capital details of the down platform canopy. The capita are not identical to those at Braintree (*ERH* p.45).

Above: Both canopies were wholly re-roofed in 1985. This gave the opportunity for clear view of the construction of the 1903 up side section, which like many other 'lat GER 'standard' canopies had steel transverse as well as longitudinal girders (RSJs)

CHINGFORD

Opposite top: The 1878 Chingford buildings were designed by Edward Wilson & Co and were very much a 'one-off', and quite different in spirit from the Palace Gates lir stations produced by them in the same year. The most notable features were the inset ground floor windows under segmental arches, and the coving under the eaves with i incised floral decoration. In this Edwardian view the building is still in original condition.

Opposite middle: In the late LNER period the Booking Hall was enlarged and a second doorway replaced a pair of windows; also the entrance canopy was added which laste until the 1979 alterations. The doorway to the Parcels Office (right of lamp post) had also replaced a window. By this late 1950s view, three of the original elaborate chimney (left) had been replaced, and the remaining two (right) would soon follow. The narrower door to the left of the canopy was the entrance to the Station Master's flat.

D.J. Taylor collectio

One thing that Chingford did share with the Palace Gates branch buildings was the use of 'Mk 1' 'standard' valancing, for which see *ERH* p.44. Indeed, these were the very first stations to have it. Here we see the Chingford down side canopy in the 1900s. Unfortunately the valancing was removed pre-electrification.

Above: The Chingford canopy however has brackets to this unique (?) design. The columns are similar to those at Dovercourt, Brentwood, and Buckhurst Hill (*ERH* pp. 43/44), save for the minimal decoration of the capitals, and a higher base section.

Right: The down side canopy was supported on the buildings at the rear throughout, but the up side canopy extended well beyond the short building on that side and so has double columns for much of its length.

Detail of upstairs windows and eaves decoration in the 1878 building. Note the two pendant ballflowers.

The main part of the single-storey south end of the 1878 building originally ended to the right of the triple windows (SM's Office) after which there was a narrower set-back Gents. The LNER built a new Gents immediately to the south (replaced by the present block in 1979) and extended the main building over the site of the old Gents, to provide a Porters' Room and replacement Newsagent's stall. The brick is a slightly darker red than the bright red 1878 brickwork.

16. THE 1872 EDMONTON [ENFIELD] LINE

CONSTRUCTION OF THE HACKNEY DOWNS LINES

The GER's Metropolitan Station and Railways Act 1864 authorised the extension to Liverpool Street (Railways Nos 1 and 2), the Bethnal Green - Edmonton Junction line (Railway No. 3), the Hackney Downs - Wood Street line (Railway No. 8), and several curves, at the huge total cost of £2m. A contract was given to Lucas Bros for all these lines in February 1865, and work commenced, but was continually held back by delays in land acquisition. In November Lucas complained 'we shall soon be at a standstill'. However by March 1866 £93,565 of work had been certified complete by Sinclair. Only £47,466 had been paid, but that was nothing unusual, and the principal cause of the actual suspension of work in summer 1866 was rather that, following the national financial crisis, the GER no longer had money to continue buying land.

In this initial period the only work done was on three sections of line in the Hackney Downs / Rectory Road area, as shown on the 1870 OS here; plus most of the earthworks and bridges on the Wood Street line between Hall Farm Jn and Shern Hall Street, but no maps are known showing this line as abandoned in 1866, the First Edition OS having been done earlier.

The original design work on the viaducts and other main structures was clearly done in 1864-6 under the then GER Engineer Robert Sinclair, who was authorised to prepare the contract plans in November 1864. (This work however may have excluded the girder bridge details, and almost certainly, given normal practice, excluded any details of station buildings). In 1866 Sinclair resigned as Engineer but was retained as Consulting Engineer for the new lines until 1868, when he retired fully. Responsibility for new lines was then handed to the GER's new Consulting Engineers Edward Wilson & Co (appointed July 1868), and it was they who developed the distinctive standard station building designs for which the Enfield and Wood Street lines have always been known.

The precise alignment of the viaduct between the Bethnal Green Road bridge and the NLR bridge was changed at most points by the GER's 1870 Act, and this must have involved a largescale redesign of the viaduct and bridges over this section. This Act also extended the time limit for completion of the new lines to 1872/1873. By the end of 1869 the GER's finances had recovered sufficiently to be able to permit the resumption of the works on the new lines. (The Hall Farm Jn - Shern Hall Street section of the Walthamstow line, the line for which there was most public pressure, was completed separately, still by Lucas Bros, in 1869/70 and opened in April 1870).

Lucas Bros recommenced work under a new contract (at 7½% less than the 1865 prices) as follows:

February 1870 Richmond Road (north of London Fields) to West Green Road (Seven Sisters)
June 1870 Bethnal Green Jn to Richmond Road
September 1870 West Green Road to Edmonton Jn
nk Hackney Downs to Hall Farm Jn
(December 1870 Liverpool Street to Bethnal Green).

In November 1870 the GER Board was told that 'the works north of the existing viaduct at Bethnal Green are in active progress, and a considerable part of the new lines might be completed by the summer of next year'.

Whilst this proved overoptimistic, it is clear that the *viaducts* were pretty much complete by the end of 1871, and the date '1871' is given for them in the tabulation here. The *girder bridges* were erected at various dates 1870-72: a letter from J.H. Bazalgette (as Engineer to the Metropolitan Board of Works) in August 1870 reveals that 'some few' had already been completed by then, in contrast, when the directors went over Railway No.3 in January

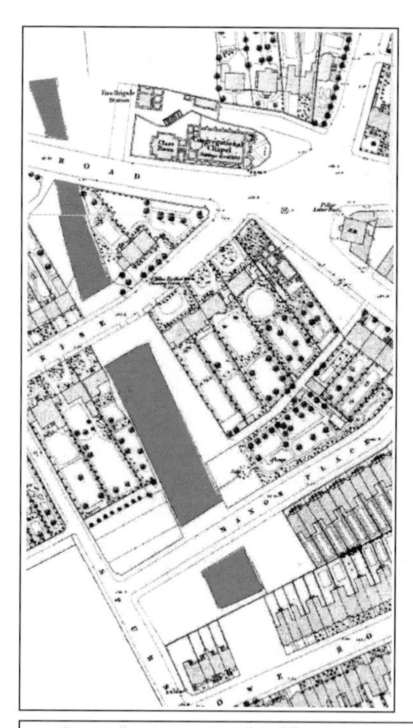

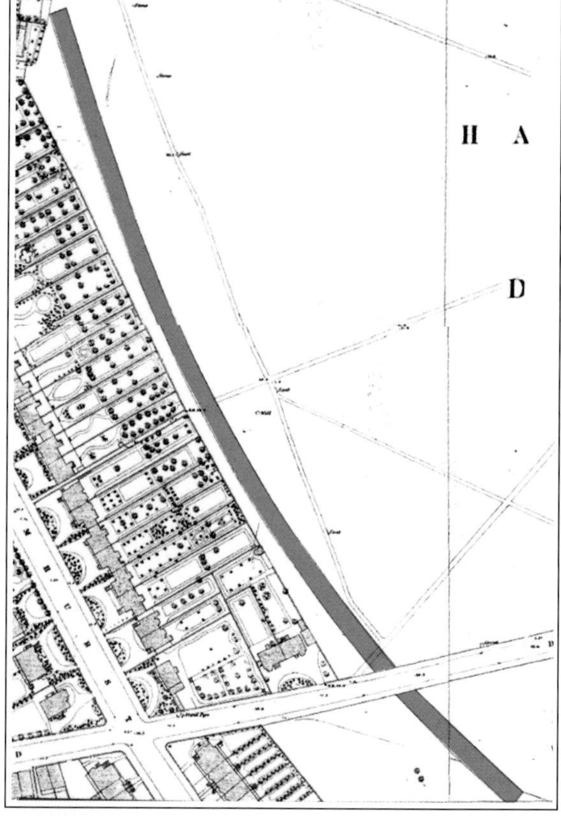

THE 1865/6 WORKS

(1870 OS)

The portions of the viad[uct] constructed (or 'partially constructe[d'] to quote the 1869 deposited plans[)] 1865/6 are shaded grey.

Left: At Hackney Downs station 2[…] yards of viaduct (arches 437-4[…]) were erected, including t[he] abutments of the Manor Pla[ce] Dalston Lane ('Rise'), and Amhu[rst] Road bridges. (100 yards to the inc[h])

Middle: To the north a 500 ya[rd] section of viaduct was built fr[om] arch 471 south of Downs Pa[rk] Road to Arch 504 south of Dow[ns] Road. (100 yards to the inch).

Bottom: Then for 400 yards fro[m] Evering Road overbridge at '[…] (which appears to be part-built) [to] Stoke Newington Common th[e] formation was fenced off b[ut] seemingly little else done. Everi[ng] Road was a new road that w[as] required to access Rectory Ro[ad] station. Note the large area [of] brickfield[s] here. Thes[e] are almo[st] certainly th[e] Lucas Br[os] brickfield[s] which th[e] GER mad[e] payment f[or] in 1866 (f[or] 'the mone[y] expended i[n] plant and i[n] buying lan[d] for brickfield[s] to execut[e] the contract[']. This wa[s] the neares[t] area of ope[n] fields to th[e] main sectio[n] of viaduct. Th[e] structures i[n] the field[s] north o[f] Evering Road ar[e] probabl[y] the bric[k] kilns; th[e] roadway t[o] them from Rectory Roa[d] looks new (200 yards t[o] the inch).

372 they found that 'many of the bridges are still to be put up'. In ne tabulation all the girder bridges are dated '1871'. As to the *ation buildings*, they were not completed until opening. Lucas ras castigated by the GER in January 1872 re 'the slow progress of ne stations, particularly as regards the awnings'.

After four inspections by Capt. Tyler, the lines were opened:

Bethnal Green - Stoke Newington	May 1872
Hackney Downs Jn - Coppermill Jn	June 1872
Stoke Newington - Edmonton Jn (and doubling of Edmonton n - Enfield)	July 1872
Clapton Jn - Hall Farm Jn	August 1872

'HE 1866/1871 VIADUCTS

The arch numbering system probably dates from 1872 (it is ised in the 1883 Bridge Book). The numbering follows on from 97 at Morpeth St on the Colchester line. As elsewhere on the GER, ridges have an 'arch number' even if they were always girder ridges.

Arches 437-452 and 471-504 were built (or part-built) in 865/6, the rest in 1870/1.

The viaduct consisted of the following sections:

198 (Bethnal Green Jn) to 427 (north of Reading Lane): 2640 rards. Of which:

198-199 were widenings of the Colchester line viaduct (Arches 137-138). (After 1893, 200 was no longer separate either).

285-302 were the wider viaduct for Cambridge Heath station

382-399 were the wider viaduct for London Fields station

then embankment

428/429 at Wilton Way

then embankment

430 Graham Rd bridge (an isolated girder bridge, but included in the arch numbering)

then embankment

431 (NLR bridge) to 512 (north of Downs Rd): 1210 yards. Of which:

435-444 were the wider viaduct for Hackney Downs station (four tracks plus side platforms).

Then no further sections of viaduct until

513 (Kings Rd) to 536 (Orchard Place): 306 yards.

On the Wood St line the only numbered viaduct arches are 537 and 540-544 (*alias* 539-543) either side of the River Lea bridge.

TOTAL 339 (Edmonton line) + 7 (Wood St line) numbered arches, however 22 of them were girder bridges, therefore the actual number of *arches* was 324. All these still exist, however the section 476-504 north of Hackney Downs was tipped over to create an embankment in 1961-3 (photos p.205).

The November 1869 GER Deposited Plans show the structure of the Hackney Downs station viaduct (as abandoned in 1866) rather better, distinguishing the two platform viaducts from the four-track main viaduct in between. (The two centre lines without platforms were only opened in 1876 in the event). It is not clear why the piers are only shown for the up platform viaduct, though. (West at top: Dalston Lane at right).

Above: As with other viaducts, the majority of the arches in the 1871 viaduct have long since been bricked up / boarded in for tenancies. However this run of still-open standard 30ft 5-ring arches survives north from Ash Grove bridge, starting with Arch 336 at right. The parapet wall has been removed here.

Bottom right: Standard 30ft 5-ring Arch 342 survives in near-original state, retaining the 'GER 1870' drainpipe head (see p.223) in the standard 4ft width right hand pier – few of these survive away from the stations. The inset drainpipes in every pier were intended as an improvement on the drainage of earlier viaducts. (The 1865/6 sections seem not to have had them). The parapet wall looks at least partly original. The road through this arch (Bush Road) was only made recently.

Above: One of the 8ft wide buttressed 'stop piers' that were provided at points where the arch sizes change (these are listed at p.201 top). 5-ring 30ft Arch 225 at right, 4-ring 21ft Arch 226 at left. Note the much higher springing point of the 21ft arches.

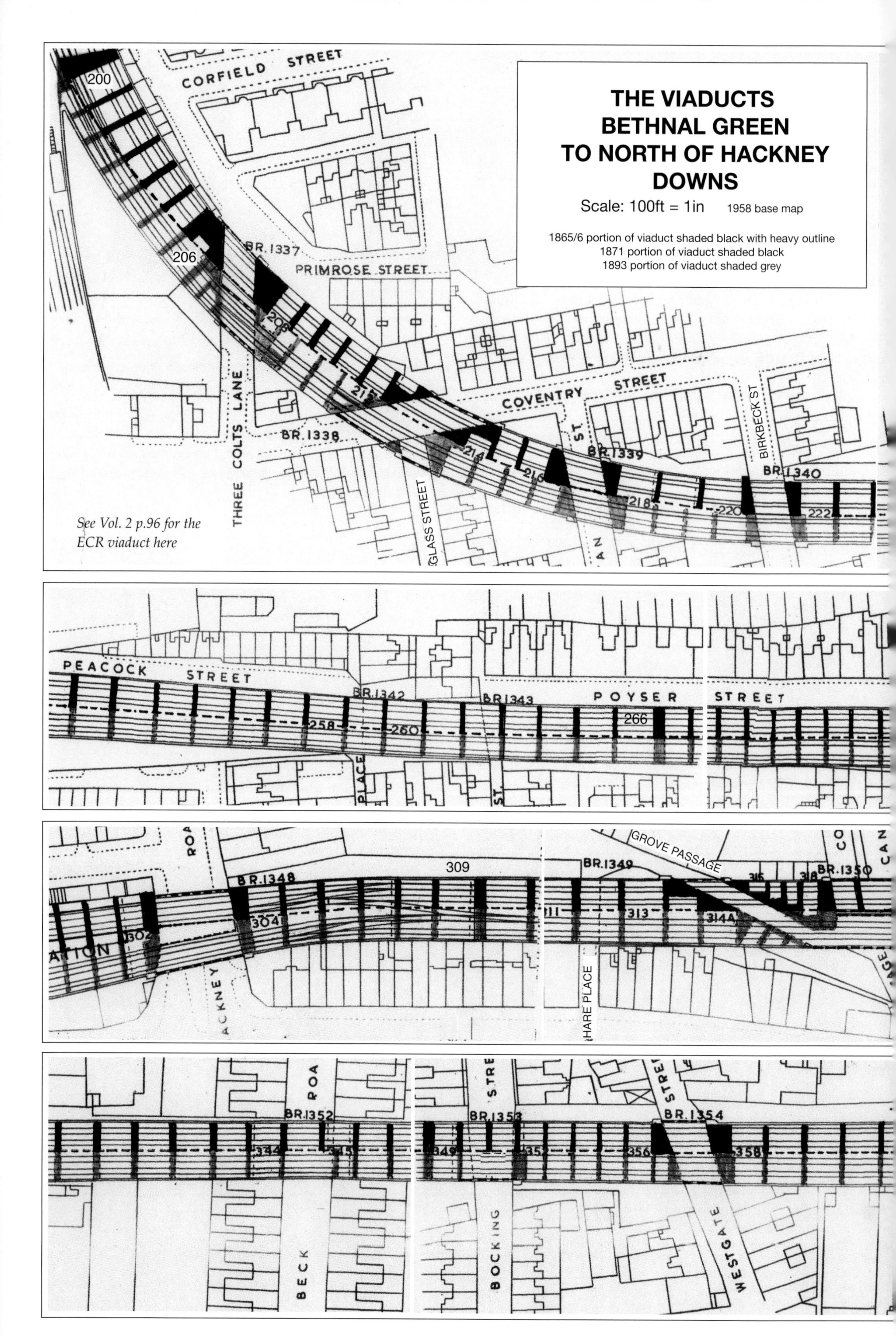

THE VIADUCTS
BETHNAL GREEN
TO NORTH OF HACKNEY
DOWNS
Scale: 100ft = 1in
1958 base map
1865/6 portion of viaduct shaded black with heavy outline
1871 portion of viaduct shaded black
1893 portion of viaduct shaded grey
CORFIELD STREET
PRIMROSE STREET
COVENTRY STREET
THREE COLTS LANE
GLASS STREET
BIRKBECK ST
BR.1337
BR.1338
BR.1339
BR.1340
See Vol. 2 p.96 for the ECR viaduct here
PEACOCK STREET
POYSER STREET
BR.1342
BR.1343
BR.1348
BR.1349
BR.1350
GROVE PASSAGE
HARE PLACE
BR.1352
BR.1353
BR.1354
BECK
BOCKING
WESTGATE

DESCRIPTION OF THE 1866/1871 VIADUCTS

Stock brick, English bond, c. 27ft 3in standard width.

4ft wide piers standard. 8ft wide buttressed piers where arch sizes change - 225/6 (photo p.199), 266/7, 309/10, 348/9.

30ft span arches standard.

Several runs of 21ft (actually 20ft 10in) span arches: 208-212, 214-216, 226-241, 267-279, 285-302 (Cambridge Heath station), 349-356, 381-403 (London Fields station), 410-415, 514-524, and 526-535.

Several runs of 35ft span arches: 281-284, 310-313, 435-437, 439-444* (Hackney Downs station, mostly 1865/6), and 476-507* (mostly 1865/6).

A few arches of other spans to fit local constraints (23ft / 25ft / 29ft).

21ft arches are 4-ring, 30ft arches 5-ring, 35ft arches 6-ring (5-ring in the 1865/6 portions).

No skew arches save for the four road bridges listed at table p.207, also 428/510/512 next to bridges.

There is no decoration save for the alternate use of red brick courses in the arches of the original road bridges. Throughout the viaduct there is a five-course proud string course of ordinary stock brick.

*There is no local reason for non-standard arch length on these two sections, and this rather suggests that 35ft had been intended as the standard span when work began in 1865.

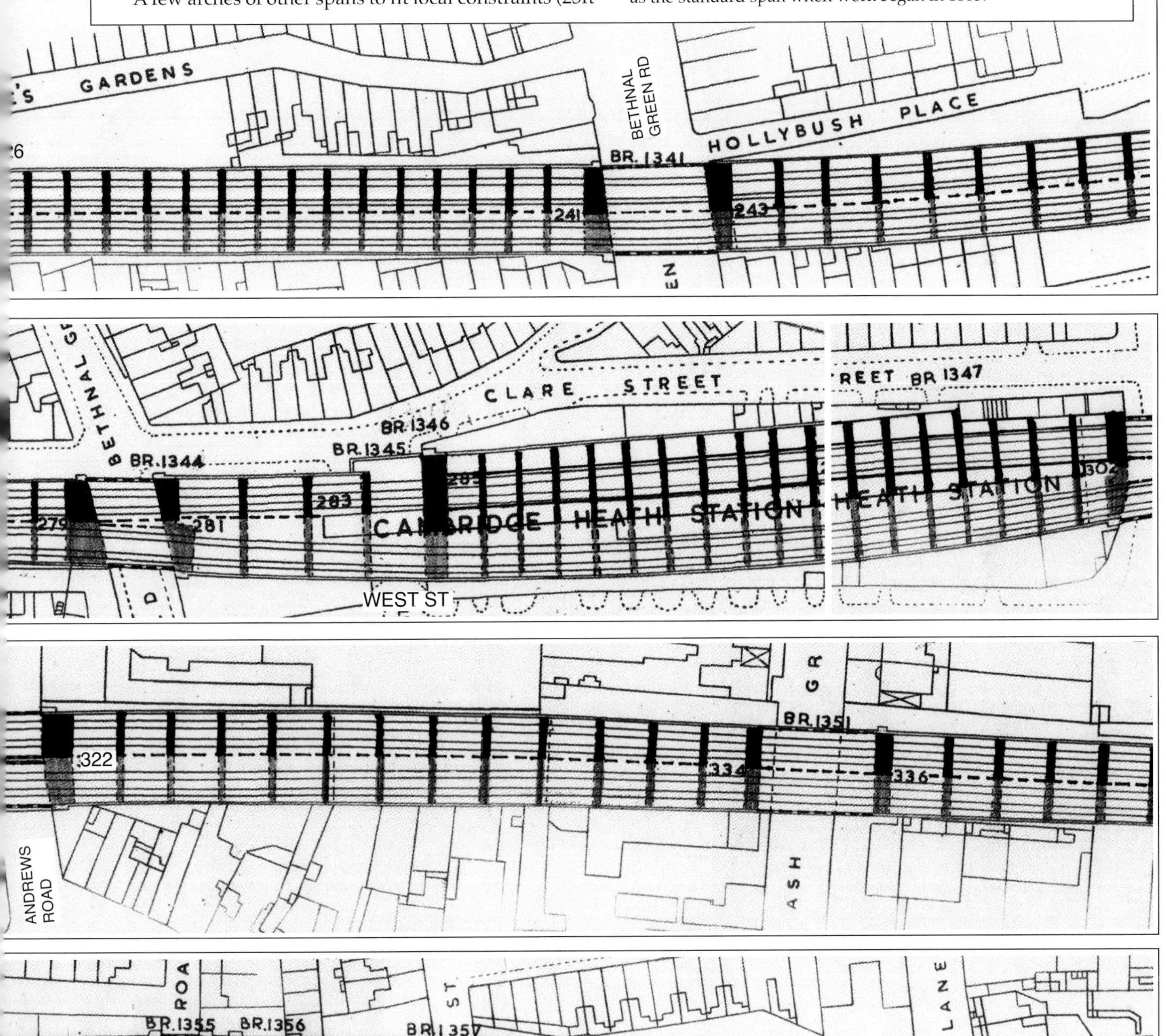

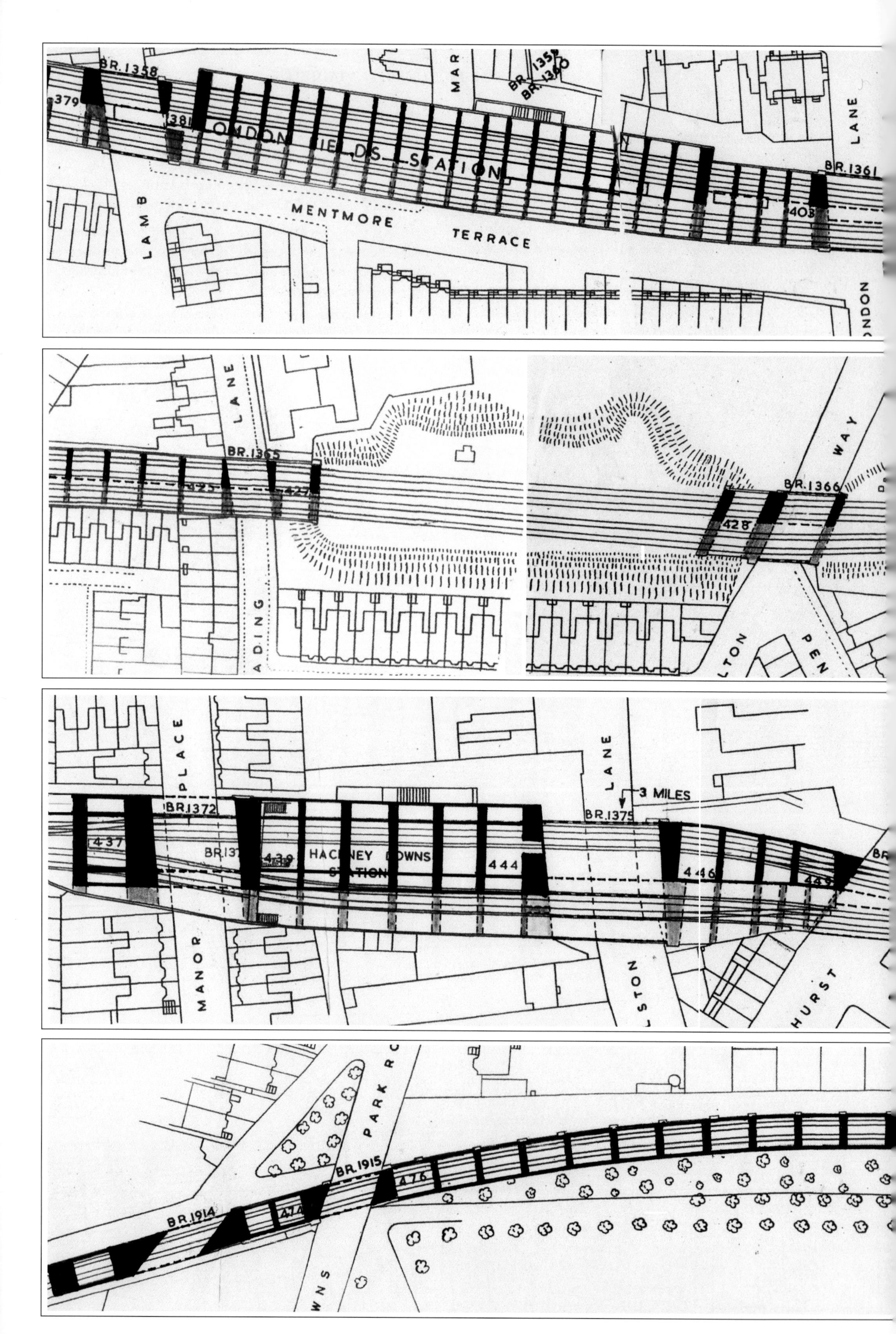
BR.1358
379
381
LONDON FIELDS STATION
BR.1359
BR.1360
MENTMORE
TERRACE
LAMB
LANE
BR.1361
403
LANE
BR.1365
425
427
BR.1366
428
WAY
PLACE
BR.1372
437
HACKNEY DOWNS STATION
444
LANE
3 MILES
BR.1375
446
MANOR
HURST
PARK
BR.1915
476
BR.1914

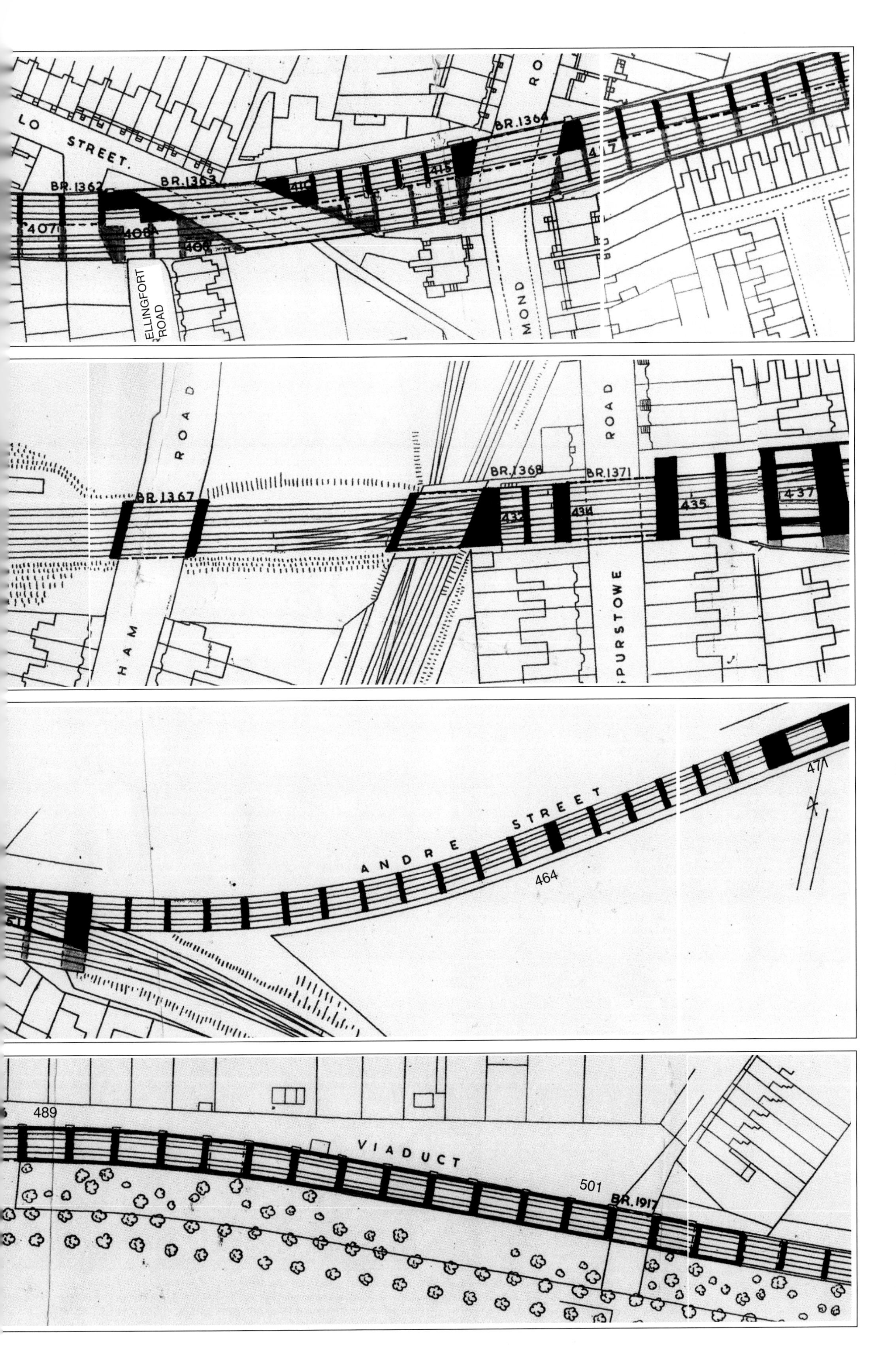
LO
STREET.
BR.1362
BR.1363
BR.1364
407
408A
408
410
415
417
ELLINGFORT ROAD
MOND
RO
ROAD
BR.1367
BR.1368
BR.1371
432
434
435
437
ROAD
HAM
SPURSTOWE
ANDRE STREET
464
489
VIADUCT
501
BR.1917

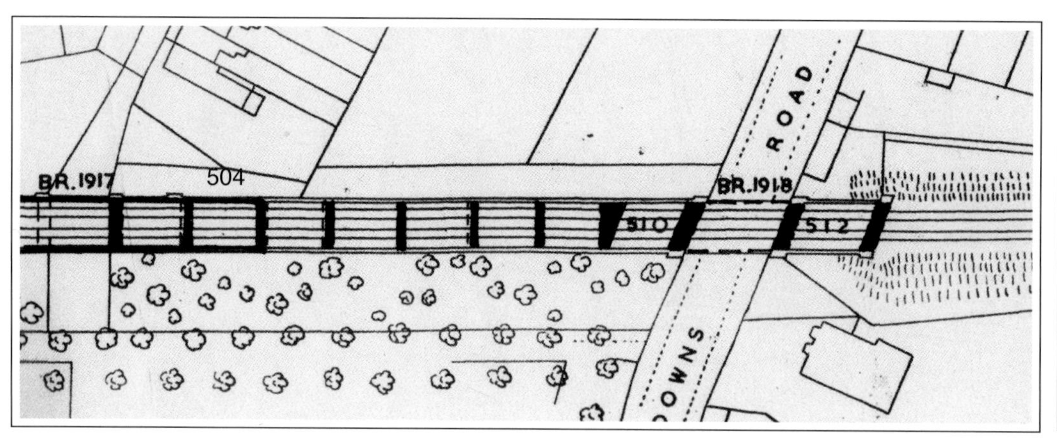

below

VIADUCT BETWEEN BRUCE GROVE AND WHITE HART LANE

Scale: 100ft = 1in

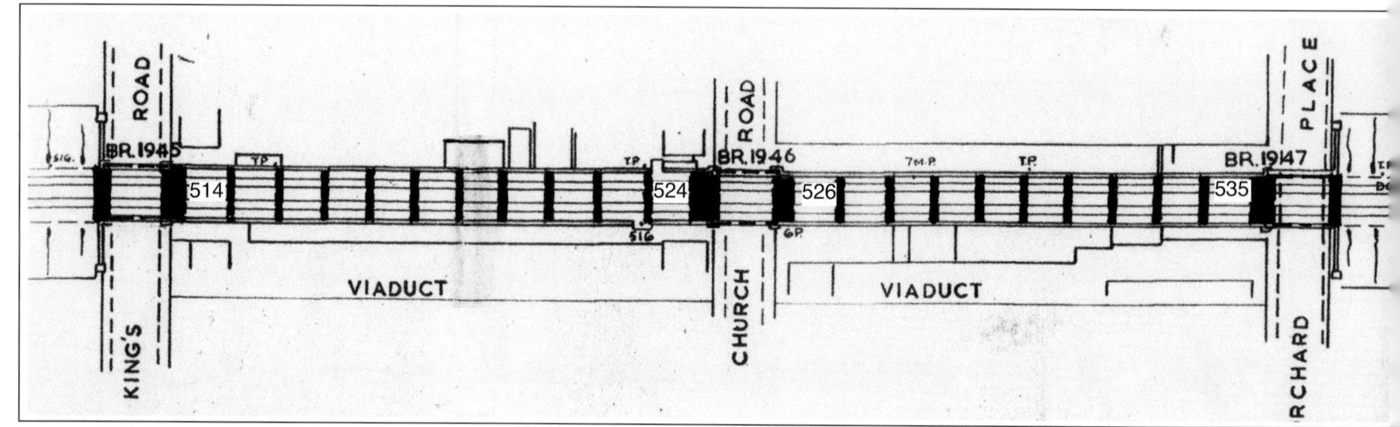

Beck Road was made through the 30ft Arch 345 in 1891, with the north side pavement passing through 346. Again there is no significant alteration from the original state here.

Essex Street (now Bocking Street) was put through Arches 350 and 351, part of a run of eight 21ft 4-ring arches, around 1880.

View north along Andre Street from Amhurst Road. 30ft Arches 451 and 452 in the foreground were (part-) built in 1865/6, and the wide buttressed pier beyond (which is shown on the 1870 OS p.198) was the northern limit of the 1865/6 work. Possibly it was made so in order to render the works stable before abandonment? This buttressed pier also marks the point at which the Chingford line embankment was tipped against the viaduct, another reason for extra solidity no doubt. There is a higher parapet wall at this point, dropping down above Arch 454.

Arches 453-470 were built in 1871, as standard 30ft 5-ring arches, to fill the gap between the two sections of viaduct erected in 1865/6. In the foreground here is the abnormally wide pier between Arches 464 and 465, the reason for which is not evident.

Between Arches 470 (off-view to right) and 471 (centre) there is another wide buttressed pier, and this represents the south end of the second portion of 1865/6 viaduct (471-504), corresponding to the buttressed pier between 452 and 453. Beyond 471 there is a length of solid wall which was the southern abutment of the very skew former girder Bridge 1914 (Arch 472). This bridge was closed as a right of way in the early C20 and filled in in 1998.

In 1961-3 the whole of Arches 476-504 north from Downs Road were tipped around to be converted to embankment. It can hardly be a coincidence that this was the section part-built in 1865/6, so perhaps they had got into poor condition as a result of early deterioration during the five year abandonment? The 1895 OS reveals that all the piers on this section had been given small buttresses, which can be seen in this 20.1.1961 view taken soon after the start of the work – no doubt a sign of early worries. Although of 35ft span, these arches were only 5-ring. At left work is under way on the concrete retaining wall for the embankment. *courtesy Andy Rush*

This southward view was taken on 18.3.1963 after completion of the work. The buildings in Downs Road can be seen in the distance. The embankment today is covered with tree growth. *courtesy Andy Rush*

In contrast the 1871-built Arches 505-510 were not replaced by embankment. They were, however, strengthened with two additional rings of brickwork below the original five. This northward view from September 1962 shows 35ft Arches 506 and 507 and 29ft Arches 508-510, with the 1958 Downs Road bridge beyond. Today these arches are scarcely visible due to tree growth, except 510 adjacent to the bridge which is wholly refaced in engineering brick. The decorative railings above 506 are a mystery!

510 and its opposite number 512 were (like 428 at Wilton Way) *skew* arches; at all the other skew girder bridges the abutments were shaped accordingly instead. *courtesy Andy Rush*

Left: Turning now to the seven arches that were *designed* as road bridges (rather than having roads put through them later), this is Bridge 1340, Birkbeck Street. Unfortunately the one decorative feature, the use of red brick in the second and fourth courses of the arch, does not show up in black and white! This bridge and 1339 have buttresses either side as a result of the skew construction.

Bridge 1357, Helmsley Place. This bridge is of only 24ft 6in span.

Left: West Street bridge (Arch 284), at the sou end of Cambridge Heath station, is one of a r of four 35ft 6-ring arches, required by the relati positions of this road and Old Bethnal Gree Road. The second, fourth, and sixth rings of th arch are red brick. Above is the 196 cantilevered down platform extension (whic partly replaced a similar 1893 extension, henc the several cut-back old brackets). At left is th south end of the 1871 down platform viaduc (See also photo opposite top).

Below (montage): Hare Row bridge (Arch 31 and the adjacent Arch 313 (left) are th northernmost of a run of four 35ft 6-ring arche There are just signs of red brick beneath th warning stripes! Martello Street bridge at far lef

Above: The west side of the Martello Terrace bridge (Arch 390), half way along the London Fields station platforms. At both Cambridge Heath and London Fields the platforms were built on higher 21ft-span 3-ring segmental arches, either side of the main viaduct arches (also 21ft span). A 'GER 1870' drainpipe head can be seen in the pier at right. The parapet wall (platform rear wall) and its buttressing are probably original.

Since 1893 the *up* platform viaducts at these two stations have not been visible, except from below at the underbridges.

Right: The platform viaducts at London Fields (Martello Terrace bridge) have these oddly-positioned relieving arches in the abutments. *Upper* photo shows the down platform (south side) abutment, and *lower* photo shows the up platform (south side) abutment, with the division between the 1871 and 1893 sections showing clearly. At left is the non-standard Fast lines girder bridge (p.213).

At West Street bridge, under the south end of the Cambridge Heath up platform, the up platform arch (centre) is 1893 work faced in engineering brick, but this is explained by the fact that the platform originally ended on the north side and was extended south over the road in 1893. 1893 Fast lines arch at left, 1871 Suburban lines arch at right.

Looking south from Martello Terrace on the west side (in continuation of the view at p.110 bottom left), showing London Fields down platform Arches 389-382). *All* the piers on this section retain their '1870' drainpipe heads. See p.209 for the east side.

The Hackney Downs station viaduct of 1865/6 is built quite differently to the 1871 Cambridge Heath and London Fields station viaducts (both illustrated opposite). It has 35ft span (5-ring) arches in both the platform viaducts and the main viaduct. Looking from the 1981 Booking Office entrance, we see here the bricked-in Arch 444, with the 1871 down side exit doorway glimpsed at far right.

BRICK ARCH ROAD UNDERBRIDGES WITHIN THE VIADUCTS BETHNAL GREEN - HACKNEY DOWNS

		1871 portion	1893 portion
1339 Witan Street	skew	30ft *	30ft
1340 Birkbeck Street	skew	30ft *	30ft
1342 Peacock Place	straight	30ft *	30ft
1343 Poyser Street	straight	30ft *	30ft
1345 West Street	straight	35ft *	35ft
1349 Hare Row	straight	35ft u*	35ft
1352 Beck Road	straight	30ft ++	c.44ft
1353 Bocking Street	straight	21ft ++	plate girder bridge
1357 Helmsley Place	skew	24ft 6in	24ft 6in
1359 Martello Terrace	straight	21ft ++	plate girder bridge
1362 Ellingfort Road	straight	30ft ++	plate girder bridge
1365 Reading Lane	skew	30ft	30ft

* Has red brick courses in arch (the original road bridges)

++ Not a road bridge in 1871 (road made later). [Reading Lane is shown as a road in the 1869 deposited plans, yet it does not appear in the 1883 Bridge Book, and has no red courses].

Other brick arch occupation / footpath underbridges on the lines opened 1872 (away from the viaduct sections) were 1916, 1917, 1938, 1957 and 1958 (photos below). Also 1890 on the Wood Street line (p.193). All are stock brick, segmental arches.

1871 BRICK ARCH UNDERBRIDGES ELSEWHERE ON THE EDMONTON LINE

There are only a few small brick arch underbridges elsewhere on this line (but see also p.193 for the identical bridges on the Walthamstow / Chingford line).

Above: Bridge 1958. Originally an occupation arch, it became 'Bridge Road' later, but is now a footway only. 16ft span 4-ring arch.

Left: Bridge 1938. Always a footpath. 6ft span 3-ring arch.

Below: Bridge 1957 was built as an occupation bridge. 13ft span 3-ring arch.

The great majority of the Edmonton line brick arch overbridges were replaced by concrete beam bridges in the pre-electrification works. Cazenove Road (Bridge 1923), over the Stoke Newington station platforms, no doubt survived because its greater span gave it a greater height.

Right upper: At Stamford Hill the 1871 overbridge for Amhurst Park, which carries the station footbridge, was also retained, avoiding the need for a new footbridge as required at Clapton (p.234) and Rectory Road (p.216).

Right lower: The south end of the cut-and-cover Stoke Newington tunnel. The track was lowered through here in 1958. The pale brickwork above is the rear of the 1974/5 station building.

THE 1894 QUADRUPLING BETHNAL GREEN - HACKNEY DOWNS

Sinclair had actually recommended in 1865 that this section of line be built 4-track from the start, but this was only done over the 495 yards from Wilton Way to Amhurst Road (Hackney Downs South Jn to Hackney Downs North Jn).

The 1870 Act had included powers to acquire land for another two lines on the east side, and the great majority of this land *was* acquired in 1870/1, as is proved by an 1887 rent roll plan.

Powers for the quadrupling were acquired under the GER's 1890 Act. Tenders for the works were opened on 17th May 1892, and that of Holme & King, at £194,680, was accepted on 21st June. The work was done in 1892-4 and the new lines were brought into use in July 1894. Maj. Gen. Hutchinson made an inspection in November 1894 and found everything satisfactory save for very minor matters. The date '1893' is given for the new structures in this book.

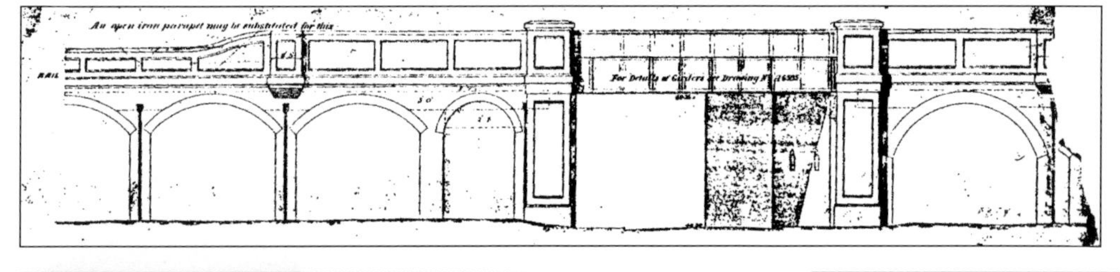

Plan for the widening, showing the new Old Bethnal Green Road bridge and the viaduct either side. There is a 12ft blind arch in the wide abutment to the left of the bridge.
courtesy Network Rail

DESCRIPTION OF THE 1893 PORTION OF THE VIADUCT BETHNAL GREEN - HACKNEY DOWNS

The arches are mostly simple widenings of the 1871 work, with the same arch numbers, however the arrangement of arches varies at certain points, mostly adjacent to skew bridges.

All faced in engineering brick. Arches have 4, 5 or 6 rings on the same basis as 1871. Width c.23ft where not affected by proximity to bridges. There is a six-course proud string course throughout, the bottom course less proud (some variations in this). No decoration, except for alternate courses of red brick in the arches at two road bridges only. No inset drainpipes in piers.

Panelled parapet walling, with stepped-out refuges.

All as per the contemporary L&B viaduct widening (*LRH* Vol. 1 p.14), which also has 30ft span segmental arches as standard.

The 1893 widening portion of the viaduct is throughout contiguous with the 1871 portion, with the join very evident thanks to the use of engineering brick instead of stock brick. Throughout it is simply added on the east side, so there are none of the complexities involved in unravelling the development of the Blackwall and ECR Colchester line viaducts. As in the 1871 section, the best run of still-open arches is north of Ash Grove, and the 1893 work is also in fully original condition over this length. We see here arches 336-341, from the south ends. The parapet wall normally rises either side of road bridges, as in the contemporary Blackwall viaduct widening. Most bridges also have 'panelled' buttresses either side, but these stand only slightly proud of the normal face of the viaduct. Some of the abutments in the 1893 portion have relieving arches, as seen here (bricked up) in the north side of Arch 336.

This closer view of Arch 336 shows the details of the brickwork in the 1893 work, although there are some variations by one or two courses. Here there are five ordinary courses above the head of the arch, then one course slightly proud, four courses further proud, and two chamfered courses. The parapet wall then begins with three ordinary courses and two chamfered courses leading into the recessed 'panel'. The L&B viaduct 1892/3 work is the same, except for omitting the bottom slightly proud course.

Left: Sequence of 21ft three-ring arches, 382-403, carrying the Fast lines past London Fields station (the west side of these arches is seen at p.207). It is not obvious why a high parapet wall was deemed appropriate at this point.

Right: The east side of Witan Street bridge (Arch 217), a five-ring 30ft arch as in the 1871 portion. The end of the high section of parapet wall over the bridge is seen at left, and there is a blind arch here in the abutment walling. Buttresses on either side. Birkbeck Street bridge is identical.

Left: As Beck Road had already been made prior to the 1893 widening, the Fast lines could be given a single arch (345), which is of c.44ft span, with six rings, and using red brick for three of the courses, which makes for quite a striking impression in strong light against the engineering brick (see back cover colour view).

View underneath at Beck Road to show the difference in length of the 1871 and 1893 Arches 345. The 1893 Arch 346 is in compensation very short, the tenancy within it being entered through this relieving arch.

Left: Helmsley Place bridge is the only other example of red brick courses in the 1893 arches. This bridge is unusual in *not* having buttresses.

Hare Row, a six-ring 35ft arch (Arch 312), is unusual in that the parapet wall reduces from high to low in the middle of the bridge! However no attractive composition would have been possible at this cramped location.

1871 SUBURBAN LINES PLATE GIRDER UNDERBRIDGES WITH UNDERSLUNG CROSS GIRDERS

The bridges on the 'Metropolitan' lines were designed by Edward Wilson & Co. The underbridges were much more numerous than the overbridges. Unusually, all but a handfu of the underbridges were built with underslung cross girders: those with spans up to 35-40ft had three main girders, those of greater span only two main girders (reflectin normal UK railways' policy of two girders only for longer spans). However, there were (as described below) more differences between the two types than was required simpl because of the number of main girders.

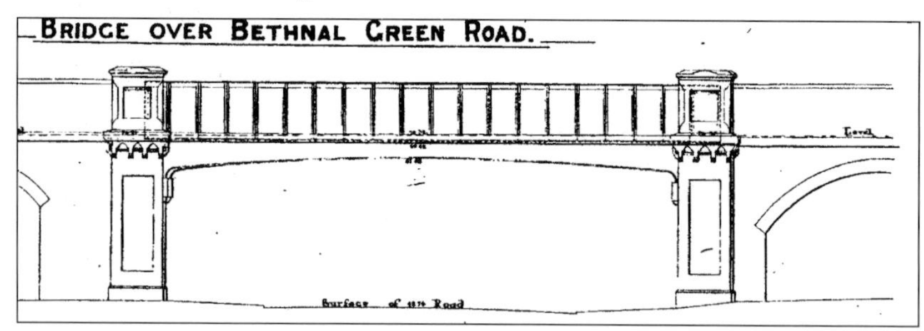

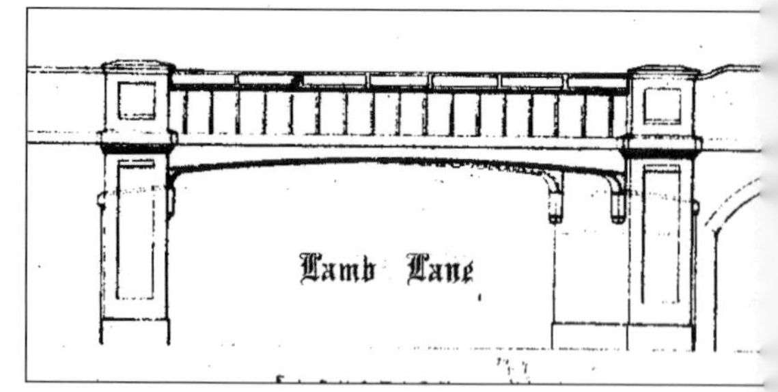

Both the two-girder and the three-girder versions had the further unusual feature of arched (three-centred, low rise) cast iron 'skirting' plates, supported on corbels on the abutments, below the main outer girders, as shown in these two drawings - *right* an original 1870 elevation of Bridge 1358 Lamb Lane (the gothic style extended to the drawings!), *left* an 1890 widening drawing showing the existing Bridge 1341 Bethnal Green Road. These plates appear to have been purely decorative, to cover from view the ends of the cross girders. They cannot have helped inspection access, and were mostly removed in the late GER or LNER periods - the only close photograph known is o Bridge 1952 Silver Street (p.228). The corbels however have remained in situ in many cases. Bethnal Green Road was one of only two bridges (the other was Hackney Road, p.211) to have the special gothic stone 'cornice' on the buttresses.
courtesy Network Rail

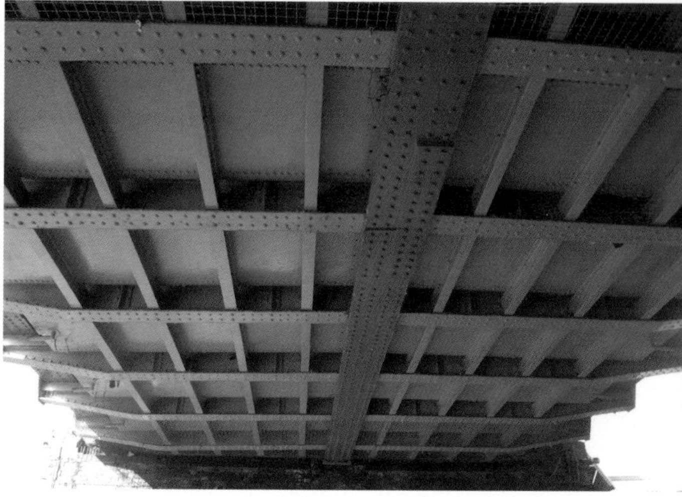

Dealing first with the shorter-span three main girder bridges, there were fewer than ten of these, of which only two, 1903 Wood St (seen in these two views) and 1948 Whitehall St, remain today. The centre girder is supported on the abutments in the normal way, and the cross girders rest on its lower flange as normal; they are only underslung in relation to the two outer girders, which (as in any three-girder bridge) bear much less of the stresses than the centre girder. A vertical plate fixed to each end of the cross girders is also bolted into the upper side of the bottom flange of the main girders. The general view shows the seven such attachment plates at Wood St, exposed to view since the cast iron plates were removed! The cross girders reduce sharply in depth at the ends. The underview shows the four longitudinal joists (RSJs) either side of the centre girder, at 2ft 4in centres; they rest on the bottom flange of the cross girders and are also fixed to the webs. The joists carry the 'bathtub' deck exactly as described below for the two-girder bridges.

Turning now to the longer two-girder bridges, there were some two dozen of these, of which eleven remain, the Suburban lines bridges at Three Colts Lane / Coventry Street / Bethnal Green Road / Old Bethnal Green Road / Hackney Road / Grove Passage / Lamb Lane / Richmond Road / Wilton Way / Amhurst Road, and Bridge 1388 Leaside Road near Clapton. *Above left* shows Bridge 1358 Lamb Lane looking east with the Suburban lines bridge in the foreground. On both abutments the two large stone corbels remain. None of the bridges of this (or the three-girder) type now have parapet plates, but some of the 1870 drawings shown them (as Lamb Lane above). *Above right* is the underside of Bridge 1337 Three Colts Lane, showing the nine longitudinal joists used in this type, which are fixed to the web of the cross girders a little way up. Drainage channels have been added suspended from the cross girders. *Right* shows details at Bridge 1960 Church St (since replaced). The cross girders reduce in depth in a curve towards the end (instead of the sharp angle of the three-girder type) and end half way across the width of the bottom flange of the main girders. The vertical plates are the same shape as in the three-girder design, but are bolted onto the underside of the bottom flange of the main girder, with the bolts in tension carrying the whole weight and stresses of the bridge. This is in principle a very unsatisfactory feature, but in practice has served happily for 145 years! This photograph also shows better the so-called 'bathtubs' (A) supported on the joists (B), in which the ballast and sleepers are laid, so that the rails are only a little above the height of the bottom flange of the main girders. This bridge, like many, has had drainage channels (C) added on each side via holes punched in the web of the cross girders.

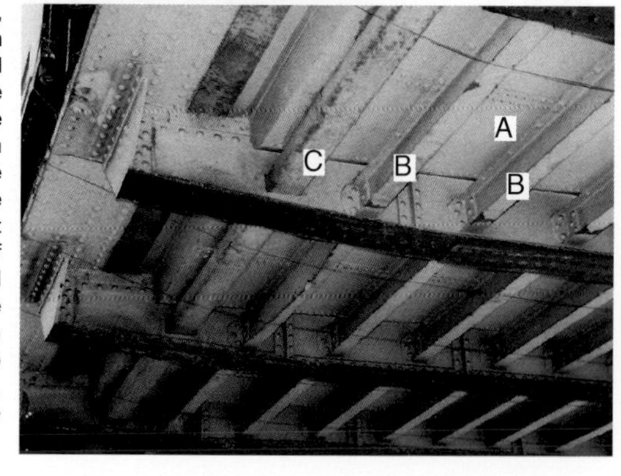

Hackney Road bridge, a longer 69ft span, has secondary vertical web stiffeners for additional strength. At right is a rare example of the full height of a buttress being retained, hiding the end of the girders from view. Almost all C19 girder bridges were so arranged originally, for better visual effect; but this makes access to the girder ends and the bearing points difficult, and in consequence the upper parts of the brickwork were removed at most bridges in the C20. The rectangular inset panels above the stone cornices are in red brick, and there is also red brick between each arch in the cornices.

Above: The very skew Grove Passage bridge, looking north. Here the old corbel is rather larger. The cross girders in this bridge are of full depth to the ends, the different design probably being related to the very heavy skew.

Right: Regents Canal Suburban lines bridge has the longest span (75ft) of all the bridges of this type, and in consequence has a more substantial type of underslung cross girder. The shorter Corbridge Crescent span at right is made to match. Again, there are secondary web stiffeners throughout here.

1871 THREE-SPAN PLATE GIRDER UNDERBRIDGES WITH CAST IRON COLUMNS

Five bridges were built in this manner in 1871, presumably because of the requirements of the highway authorities. Three (all the same) were at Hackney Downs station; Spurstowe Road and Dalston Lane were on the original four-track section, Manor (now Marcon) Place (replaced 2014) was even wider as it carried the platforms also. The others, of two-track width and to a different design, were were the lengthy very skew Martello St, and Ash Grove. None of these three-span bridges have underslung cross girders.

Above: Dalston Lane Suburban lines looking north, recently all refurbished and fitted with anti-bird wire netting. (The third cast iron column is out of shot to left: the second bridge built alongside in 1893, to the same design, is seen at right). An 1870 drawing for this bridge survives and confirms that all details are as original. Until 1893/4 the 1871 bridge carried the original four tracks, but since then it has carried the two Suburban lines and most of the width of the 1894 island platform. (Both platforms ended south of this bridge pre-1894). The construction is a 'normal' girders, cross girders, joists and plate deck type. It is a single four-track bridge, not two double-track bridges side by side. Each side of the centre girder there are eight joists with the middle two set further apart to accommodate what must be an *original* drainage channel.

Right: The second type of 1871 three-span bridge, illustrated here by Martello Street, has deeper cross girders, and the joists are fixed close to the top of the web.

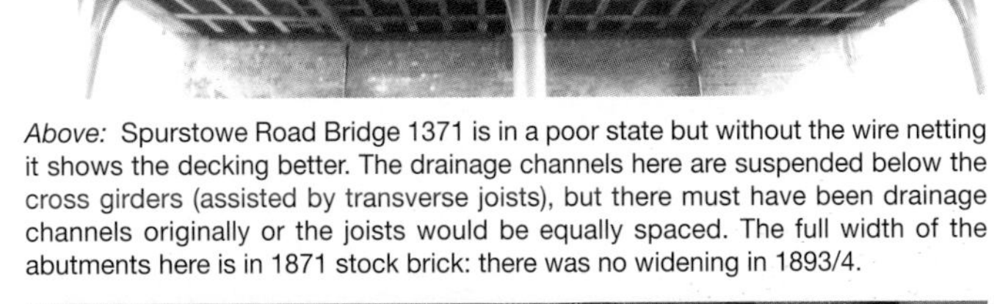

Above: Spurstowe Road Bridge 1371 is in a poor state but without the wire netting it shows the decking better. The drainage channels here are suspended below the cross girders (assisted by transverse joists), but there must have been drainage channels originally or the joists would be equally spaced. The full width of the abutments here is in 1871 stock brick: there was no widening in 1893/4.

Left: Ash Grove Suburban lines Bridge 1363. It is not evident why this unimporta road received a three-span bridge: the 1870 Act had only required a 45ft span bu the three spans are actually 16ft / 34ft / 21ft (unique in being non-symmetrical). Th construction is as per Martello St. The 1893 Fast lines bridge is also three-span an looks the same on a casual glance but the construction is as per the Lamb Lane London Lane Fast lines bridges.

THE 1893/4 WIDENING FAST LINES PLATE GIRDER UNDERBRIDGES

The 1894 MT6 inspection file has no tabulation of the new bridges, only a comment by Maj. Gen. Hutchinson that there were on the new Fast lines, in addition to the widened brick arch underbridges, 23 bridges with 'wrought iron girders and cross girders, the floors being variously constructed with jack arches or wrought iron troughing'. This was a rather 'synopsising comment and indeed he missed out one of the principal types. Apart from 1355 Warburton Rd, *all* the 1893 Fast lines bridges are still in situ. [Note the use of wrought iron still, as in the contemporary L&B work, not steel].

The jack-arched type of 1893/4 Fast lines plate girder underbridge was actually adopted only at Three Colts Lane / Old Bethnal Green Road / Bocking Street / Westgate Street / Wilton Way. This type comprises three main girders, cross girders and transverse jack arching, and plate parapets. These are all shorter span bridges, around 40ft.

Illustrated here are (left) Three Colts Lane, 30ft on the straight and very skew; and (right) the underside of Old Bethnal Green Road, which has short joists instead in the first and last sections (a 1980s alteration, as at Bocking Street).

Jack arching was much used in the 1892/3 L&B viaduct 'iron viaduct' widening, as detailed at *LRH* Vol.1 pp.17/18; but no individual road bridges there featured it, except the widened Chamber Street bridge.

There were only three 1893/4 Fast lines plate girder underbridges with troughing - Ellingfort Road, Martello Street, and Amhurst Road. The construction is two main girders, cross girders and longitudinal troughing. Martello St is a three-span bridge as per the contiguous 1871 bridge. Contemporary bridges with longitudinal troughing in the L&B quadrupling and the 1890 Colchester line widening all have *three* main girders. On those lines there are several underbridges with *transverse* troughing too, but there are no such on this line.

Left: Ellingfort Road, looking north, with the 1871 arch for the Suburban lines at left. Although only 30ft span it has quite deep cross girders, comparable to those in the 1893 Colchester line River Lea bridge (*LRH* Vol.2 p.117).

Right: Amhurst Road Fast lines bridge, with a 61ft span, is a heavier structure and differs in having a fully fishbellied bottom flange to the cross girders.

Left / Below left / Below:

Unmentioned by Hutchinson, the most numerous type of 1893 Fast lines underbridge had two main girders, cross girders, 8 or 10 longitudinal joists and plate decking. [By comparison, there is only one case of this type of decking in the contemporary L&B and Colchester line widenings, the Leman Street Fast lines bridge (*LRH* Vol. 1 p.17)].

The longer-span bridges - 1338, 1341, 1348, 1350 - had *ten* joists, five each side of an integral drainage trough. These three views show Bridge 1341 Bethnal Green Rd. The underneath view faces north, with this 1893 bridge at right and the 1871 Suburban lines bridge of the underslung cross girders type at left. The two bridges are virtually contiguous, but entirely separate constructionally. This bridge is of 69ft span.

Bethnal Green Rd is the only bridge in the Bethnal Green - Hackney Downs widening work to still sport a maker's plate. Interestingly it is not to the same pattern as the contemporary Horseley Co plate at Leman Street. Note that somebody still cared enough to 'paint in' the missing portion on the last repaint!

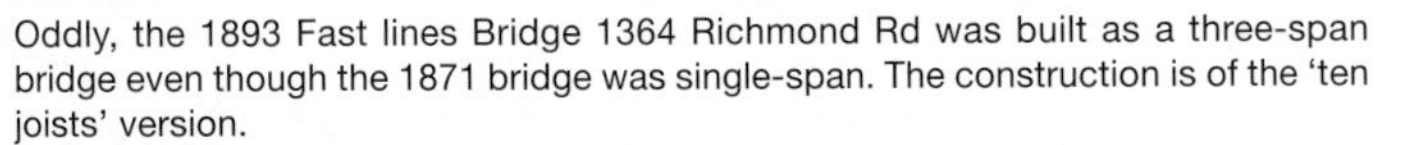

Oddly, the 1893 Fast lines Bridge 1364 Richmond Rd was built as a three-span bridge even though the 1871 bridge was single-span. The construction is of the 'ten joists' version.

Above: The other two examples of the type, London Lane (seen here) and Lamb Lane, have shorter spans (55ft and 50ft) and in consequence were deemed to require only eight joists (four either side of the integral drainage trough). Additionally the 1893 Ash Grove bridge is so constructed.

At left is the 1942 (after bomb damage) replacement London Lane Suburban lines bridge.

It was always common for very short span bridges to be built simply with multiple closely-spaced main girders. This is Martello Terrace Fast lines Bridge 1359, under London Fields station, which has six girders and is unusual in having longitudinal jack arching. There is a similar bridge of 1904 at Campbell Road (LT&SR), see *LRH* Vol. 1 p.43.

This design is found at Exmouth Place Fast lines Bridge 1356 (seen here) and the near-contemporary 1891 Lincoln Road Bridge 1987 on the Southbury Loop. Seen casually from the road they look like an ordinary plate girder bridge, but in fact the outer plates merely carry the plate parapets, and there are four main girders acting as railbearers. They are described as 'trough girders and plate floor' in the bridge records. 1355 Warburton Road was the same, but is now replaced.

(Bethnal Green) to Edmonton Junction

Opened 1872, Great Eastern Railway.

BRIDGE 1337, underbridge, Three Colts Lane, GR 349824.
Suburban lines bridge 1871, double track plate girder bridge; two main girders, underslung cross girders, nine joists, plate decking, no parapets.
Fast lines bridge 1893, double track plate girder bridge; three main girders, cross girders and transverse jack arching, plate parapets.
30ft span, very skew. (Photos pp. 210/212).

BRIDGE 1338, underbridge, Coventry Street, GR 349824.
Suburban lines bridge 1871, plate girder, two main girders, underslung cross girders, as Bridge 1337 Suburban lines.
Fast lines bridge 1893, double track plate girder bridge; two main girders, cross girders, ten joists, plate decking, plate parapets, two spans (the second over Glass St) with brick pier in between.
30ft span (57ft on skew).

BRIDGE 1339 (Arch 217), underbridge, Witan Street (formerly Parliament Street), GR 349825. Segmental arch, west side stock brick 1871, east side engineering brick 1893, 30ft span, skew. (Photo p.209).

BRIDGE 1340 (Arch 221), underbridge, Birkbeck Street, GR 349825. 1871/93, segmental arch, as Bridge 1339, skew. (Photo p. 205).

BRIDGE 1341, underbridge, Bethnal Green Road, GR 349827.
Suburban lines bridge 1871, plate girder, two main girders, underslung cross girders, as Bridge 1337 Suburban lines. (Drawing p.210).
Fast lines bridge (contiguous) 1893, double track plate girder bridge; two main girders, cross girders, ten joists, plate decking, plate parapets.
69 ft span, skew. (Photos p.213).

BRIDGE 1342 (Arch 259), underbridge, Peacock Place, GR 349829. 1871/93, segmental arch, as Bridge 1339, straight. Road closed and arch blocked.

BRIDGE 1343 (Arch 262), underbridge, Poyser Street (formerly George Street), GR 349829. 1871/93, segmental arch, as Bridge 1339, straight.

BRIDGE 1344, underbridge, Old Bethnal Green Road, GR 348831.
Suburban lines bridge 1871, plate girder, underslung cross girders, as Bridge 1337 Suburban lines.
Fast lines bridge 1893, plate girder, jack arching, as Bridge 1337 Fast lines.
40ft span (41ft 6in on skew). (Drawing p.208, photo p.212).

BRIDGE 1345 (Arch 284), underbridge, West Street, GR 348831. Segmental arches, west side stock brick 1871, 30ft span; central higher arch for up platform 1893 engineering brick; east side engineering brick 1893, straight. (Photos pp. 206/207).

CAMBRIDGE HEATH

Booking Office (road level entrance and internally) 1986. Subway (modernised 1986) 1872. Covered stairway to down platform, with waiting rooms above, 1872. New steel stairs to up platform 1986. Down platform built on high segmental arches, 1871; extended at south end, cantilevered, 1960. Base only of additional down platform building, 1894, engineering brick, three semicircular arches. [Down platform 1894 building itself demolished 1986, canopy demolished late 1960s. Up platform buildings demolished 1986, canopy demolished c.1980. 1894 red brick rear wall to up platform also now demolished].
(Photos pp. 206/207/217/223/236/240).

BRIDGE 1348, underbridge, Hackney Road, GR 348833.
Suburban lines bridge 1871, plate girder, two main girders, underslung cross girders, as Bridge 1337 Suburban lines. Fast lines bridge 1893, plate girder, joists, as Bridge 1341 Fast lines.
69ft span, skew. (Photos pp. 211/274).

BRIDGE 1349 (Arch 312), underbridge, Hare Row (formerly Hare Place), GR 348834. 1871/93, segmental arch, as Bridge 1339 but 35ft span, straight. (Photos pp. 206/209).

BRIDGE, part of Bridge 1350 (Arches 314-318), underbridge, Grove Passage, GR 347835.
Suburban lines bridge 1871, plate girder, two main girders, underslung cross girders, similar to Bridge 1337 Suburban lines but detail differences.
Fast lines bridge 1958, welded steel plate girders, concrete flooring. (Photo p.211).
Very skew.

BRIDGE 1350, underbridge, Corbridge Crescent / Regents Canal / Andrews Road, GR 347835.
Suburban lines bridge over Corbridge Crescent and Canal 1871, two spans 21ft / 75ft, double track plate girder bridge, similar in construction to Bridge 1337 Suburban lines but with heavier and more deeply underslung cross girders. Intermediate brick pier. (Photo p.211).
Suburban lines Andrews Road span 1958, as Bridge 1918, 35ft span.
Fast lines bridge 1893, plate girder, joists, as Bridge 1341 Fast lines, Corbridge Crescent / Canal is a single span except for one column on west side; separate 35ft span over Andrews Road.

BRIDGE 1351, underbridge, Ash Grove (now entrance to bus garage), GR 347837. Both bridges three spans 16ft / 34ft / 21ft with cast iron columns.
Suburban lines bridge 1871, plate girder, deep cross girders, joists set into top of cross girders, steel decking. (Photo p.212).
Fast lines bridge 1893, two main girders, cross girders and 8 joists, plate decking (details as Bridge 1358 Fast lines).

BRIDGE, no bridge number (Arch 342), underbridge, Bush Road, GR 347837. New late C20 road running through an ordinary 1871/1893 viaduct arch. (Photo p.199).

BRIDGE 1352 (Arch 345), underbridge, Beck Road, GR 347838. New road 1891 passing through an ordinary 1871 viaduct arch (north side pavement passes through Arch 346). The 1893 widening has a longer arch to cover the north side pavement also. (Photos pp. 204/209).

BRIDGE 1353 (Arches 350 and 351), underbridge, Bocking Street (formerly Essex Street), GR 347838. New road (pre-1887) running through two 21ft span 1871 viaduct arches. Fast lines bridge 1893, plate girder, jack arching, as Bridge 1337 Fast lines. (Photo p.204).

BRIDGE 1354, underbridge, Westgate Street (formerly West St), GR 347839.
Suburban lines bridge 1959, similar to Bridge 1918 but 'C1' type.
Fast lines bridge 1893, plate girder, jack arching, as Bridge 1337 Fast Lines.
40ft span, skew.

BRIDGE 1355, underbridge, Warburton Road, GR 347840.
Suburban lines bridge 1956 (1953?), as Bridge 1918, 24ft span.
Fast lines bridge BR 'Z' type 1991, two single track bridges each with two girders and concrete decking. Abutments 1956 (1953?)/1893.

BRIDGE 1356, underbridge, Exmouth Place (formerly Exmouth Street), GR 347840.
Suburban lines bridge 1956, as Bridge 1918.
Fast lines bridge u1893, four main girders acting as railbearers, plate decking, 29ft span (photo p.212).
Abutments 1956/1893.

BRIDGE 1357 (Arch 371), underbridge, Helmsley Place (formerly Helmsley Street), GR 347841. 1871/93, segmental arch, as Bridge 1339 but 24ft 6in span, skew. (Photos pp. 205/209).

BRIDGE 1358, underbridge, Lamb Lane, GR 347842.
Suburban lines bridge 1871, plate girder, two main girders, underslung cross girders, as Bridge 1337 Suburban lines. (Photo p.210).
Fast lines bridge 1893, double track plate girder bridge, two main girders, cross girders and eight joists, plate decking, no parapets.
49ft 6in span (51ft 9in on skew).

LONDON FIELDS

Booking Office 1894 (within Fast lines viaduct), frontage to Mentmore Terrace 1894, interior 1986. Subway 1876/94. New steel stairs to down platform 1986, corrugated roofing. Down platform built on high segmental arches, 1871; both platforms extended at north end 1960, cantilevered. Up plfm stairs u1872, roofing 1986. [1872 down platform waiting rooms building and canopy demolished 1985. 1894 up platform building and canopy demolished 1985]. (Photos pp. 206/207/237/240).

BRIDGE 1359 (Arch 390), underbridge, Martello Terrace, GR 347843.
New road pre-1893 passing through 1871 high segmental arch for down platform, ordinary 1871 viaduct arch, and 1871 high segmental arch for

up platform.
Fast lines bridge u1893, six main girders, longitudinal jack arching. All 21ft span. (Photos pp.206/213).

BRIDGE 1361, underbridge, London Lane, GR 347844.
Suburban lines bridge 1942 (after bomb damaged previous bridge), double track plate girder bridge, three riveted main girders, concrete flooring, no parapets.
Fast lines bridge 1893, double track plate girder bridge, two main girders, cross girders and 8 joists, plate decking (as Bridge 1358 Fast Lines), plate parapets. (Photo p.213).
55ft span.

BRIDGE 1362 (Arch 408), Ellingfort Road, GR 347845.
New road u1878 passing through ordinary 1871 viaduct arch.
Fast lines bridge 1893, double track plate girder bridge, two main girders cross girders and longitudinal troughing, 30ft span. (Photo p.212).

BRIDGE 1363, underbridge, Martello Street (formerly Tower Street), GR 347845. Three spans 12ft / 26ft / 12ft (on the straight), extremely skew. Both bridges have two sets of two round cast iron intermediate columns.
Suburban lines bridge 1871, plate girder, deep cross girders, joists set into top of cross girders, steel decking. (Photo p.211).
Fast lines bridge 1893, two main girders, cross girders and longitudinal troughing.

BRIDGE 1364, underbridge, Richmond Road, GR 347845.
Suburban lines bridge 1871, plate girder, two main girders, underslung cross girders, as Bridge 1337 Suburban lines.
Fast lines bridge 1893, three spans with two sets of two round cast iron intermediate columns, two main girders, cross girders ten joists and plate decking, plate parapets. (Photo p.213).
66ft span (77ft 6in on skew).

BRIDGE 1365 (Arch 426), underbridge, Reading Lane (formerly Grove Lane), GR 347847. 1871/93, segmental arch, as Bridge 1339, skew. Upper parts rebuilt.

[Great Eastern Buildings in Reading Lane, west of bridge, 1892 housing for those displaced by the quadrupling, demolished c.2012].

BRIDGE 1366, underbridge, Wilton Way (formerly Wilton Road, formerly Pigwell Path), GR 347847.
Suburban lines bridge 1871, plate girder, two main girders, underslung cross girders, as Bridge 1337 Suburban lines.
Fast lines bridge 1893, plate girder, jack arching, as Bridge 1337 Fast lines.
40ft span (44ft 6in on skew).

BRIDGE 1367, underbridge, Graham Road, GR 344848. Completely rebuilt 1959. Four single-track bridges contiguous, each two main girders, 50ft span (52ft on skew). 1871 stock brick abutments. (Photo p.218).

BRIDGE 1368, underbridge, North London line, GR 346849. 1930, plate girder. 50ft span (55ft on skew).

[Hackney Exchange Office B.O. building demolished 2008].

BRIDGE 1371, underbridge, Spurstowe Road, GR 346849. Four-track bridge 1871. Three spans 14ft / 46ft / 14ft with two rows of three round cast iron intermediate columns. Plate girder, three main girders, cross girders and joists, plate decking, plate parapets. (Photo p.211).

BRIDGE 1372, underbridge, Marcon Place (formerly Manor Place), GR 346850. New 2014, 'U' type, welded steel plate girder, seven bridges for platforms and tracks.

HACKNEY DOWNS

Booking Office building at street level, white brick with hipped roof, 1981; also 1981 passageway to subway. [Previous Booking Hall area walled off but still as before structurally]. Subway and stairs to island platform and Up Fast platform 1894. Down Suburban platform building, covered stairway with waiting rooms block above, and platform canopy 1872. Canopy extended at south end by two bays 1895, in original style. Valancing straightened at bottom 1950s. Island platform building and canopies 1894, 'large circle' brackets on building, otherwise 'standard' columns and brackets, new roofing 1983 (when canopy reduced in length at south end). Up Fast platform buildings and canopy 1894, 'standard' columns and brackets, new roofing 1983 (when canopy reduced in length at south end by two bays). (Photos pp. 217/237/242).

Signal box BR(ER) Type 18 power box, 1960, disused.
BRIDGE 1375, underbridge, Dalston Lane, GR 345851.
West side bridge 1871, carrying Suburban lines and most of width of island platform: plate girder, three main girders, cross girders and plate decking. 1871 stock brick abutments. 53ft wide.
[Intermediate higher section carrying rest of width of island platform].
East side bridge 1893, same type but two main girders. 1893 engineering brick abutments.
[On far east side, higher section carrying Up Fast platform, cross girders (supported on the main bridge) and concrete decking].
Both the main bridges have three spans of 29ft / 47ft / 29ft (on skew), with intermediate round cast iron columns (two rows of three on west side, two of two on east side). A sixth column in each row supports the east side of the Up Fast platform bridge. (Photo p.211).

BRIDGE 1376, underbridge, Amhurst Road, GR 345852.
Suburban lines bridge 1871, plate girder, two main girders, underslung cross girders, as Bridge 1337 Suburban lines.
Fast lines bridge 1893, plate girder, two main girders cross girders and transverse troughing (photo p.212).
61ft span, skew.

BRIDGE 1915, underbridge, Downs Park Road, GR 343855. 1958, welded steel plate girder, three main girders and concrete flooring. 1866 stock brick abutments. 40ft 3in span (48ft 3in on skew).

Bridges 1916 and 1917, underbridges, footpaths, reconstructed as 8ft concrete spans when embankment made 1961-3.

BRIDGE 1918, underbridge, Downs Road, GR 341859. 1958, welded steel plate girder, three main girders and concrete flooring. 1871 stock brick abutments. 42ft span (46ft on skew).

BRIDGE 1919, overbridge, Evering Road, GR 340862. Reconstructed 1957, concrete beams, concrete flooring. 25ft span.

RECTORY ROAD

Booking Office building at street level 1984/5, but lower parts 1872 and incorporates 1958 covered footbridge to down side. Steel stairways, down side c.1980, up side 1984/5. Platform shelters 1984/5. [Remainder of 1872 B.O. building, 1872+ down platform buildings and residue of down platform canopy, and up platform building and canopy demolished 1984 - photos pp. 216/234/236/237/243/244].

BRIDGE 1920, overbridge, Brooke Road, GR 339864. 1958, as Bridge 1919.

BRIDGE 1921, overbridge, Stoke Newington Common, GR 339865. 1957, as Bridge 1919.

BRIDGE 1922, overbridge, Northwold Road, GR 338867. 1957, as Bridge 1919.

Walled cutting between Northwold Road and Stoke Newington station.

BRIDGE 1923, overbridge, Cazenove Road, GR 337868. 1871, stock brick, segmental arch, panelled parapet walls, 36ft span. (Photo p.208).

STOKE NEWINGTON

Booking Office building at street level (pale brick, glass cladding, flat roof) 1974/5. Platform stairways 1872 [roofing removed 1974/5]. Small platform canopies 1974/5. Retaining walls behind both platforms 1871/2, stock brick, segmental arches.
[1872 main building, up platform building, and both platform canopies demolished 1973/4 - photos pp. 208/235].

BRIDGE 1924, overbridge, Stoke Newington Tunnel (cut and cover), 77 yards, GR 336869. 1871, stock brick, segmental arch. 25ft span. (Photo p.208). Wing walls at north end rebuilt 1943.

BRIDGE 1925, overbridge, Fairholt Road (actually Dunsmure Road), GR 333874. 1957, as Bridge 1919.

BRIDGE 1926, overbridge, Amhurst Park, GR 334879. 1871, stock brick, segmental arch, 25ft span. (Photo p.208).

STAMFORD HILL

Booking Office building at street level and covered footbridge 1872, refurbished 1979, interior 1979. Small flat-roof shop at west end 1880s. Steel stairways 1984. Platform shelters 1984. (Photos pp. 208/233/243).

[Down and up platform buildings, and residue of platform canopies, demolished 1984. Up platform stairway and shop at east end of frontage demolished 2011].

BRIDGE 1927, underbridge, St Ann's Road, GR 334883. 1958, as Bridge 1918. 36ft span (39ft on skew).

BRIDGE 1928, underbridge, Tottenham & Hampstead line (T&H Bridge 2012A), GR 334885. Three spans 25ft/25ft/25ft, brick abutments and piers. Middle span BR 'Z' type 1984. Side spans concrete.

BRIDGE 1930, underbridge, Seven Sisters Road, GR 334887. 1959, two single track welded steel box girder deck span bridges. 51ft span (71ft on skew). 1959 yellow brick abutments, 1871 stock brick wing walls. (Photo p.218).

SEVEN SISTERS

Underground ticket hall 1968. Down and up platform buildings / canopies 1979/80. [1872 platform buildings and residue of canopies demolished 1984 - photos pp. 225/226/244].

BRIDGE 1934, underbridge, West Green Road, GR 334890. c.1998, as Bridge 1939.

BRIDGE 1935, overbridge, Clyde Road, GR 334895. 1957, as Bridge 1919.

BRIDGE 1936, overbridge, Philip Lane, GR 334896. 1958, as Bridge 1919.

BRIDGE 1937, underbridge, Forster Road, GR 336899. 1958, as Bridge 1918.

BRIDGE 1938, underbridge, footpath, GR 337899. 1871, stock brick, segmental arch, 6ft span. (Photo p.207).

BRIDGE 1939, underbridge, St Loy's Road, GR 337899. Reconstructed 1998, welded steel plate girder, two single line bridges each with two main girders, cross girders and steel plate decking, concrete protection beams on outside. 40ft span. (Photo p.218).

BRUCE GROVE

Booking Office building at street level 1872, extended on east side 1888. Interior 1979. Brick stairways to platforms 1872 [roofing removed 1981]. Up platform building and canopy 1872, canopy reduced in length 1981, new roofing 2000. Down platform canopy 2000, in 1872 style, three bays. (Photos pp. 224/227/236/243/244/245).

BRIDGE 1941, underbridge, Bruce Grove, GR 338901. 1903, plate girder, two main girders, cross girders and nine joists, plate decking. 50ft span (57ft on skew). Abutments 1871 south side / 1903 north side.

BRIDGE 1942, underbridge, Pembury Road, GR 337904. 1958, as Bridge 1918.

BRIDGE 1943, underbridge, Lordship Lane, GR 337906. 1998, as Bridge 1939.

BRIDGE 1944, underbridge, Ruskin Road, GR 337908. 1998, as Bridge 1939.

BRIDGE 1945, underbridge, King's Road, GR 337909. 1958, as Bridge 1918.

VIADUCT between Bridges 1945 and 1946, and Bridges 1946 and 1947 (Arches 514-524 and 526-535). 1871, stock brick, segmental arches (four ring), 21ft span. Plan p.204.

BRIDGE 1946, underbridge, Church Road, GR 337910. 1958, as Bridge 1918.

BRIDGE 1947, underbridge, Orchard Place, GR 337911. 1958, as Bridge 1918.

BRIDGE 1948, underbridge, Whitehall Street, GR 337912. 1871, three main girders, underslung cross girders (see p.210). 35ft span.

WHITE HART LANE

Booking Office building at street level 1978. Steel stairways 1978. Up platform building and canopy 1872. Down platform canopy 1872, three bays only remain. Both canopies have replacement roofing and valancing u1978. (Photos pp. 224-7/239/241).

Station Master's house on north side of White Hart Lane, date nk. Block of three coal offices adjacent, 1883.

BRIDGE 1950, underbridge, White Hart Lane, GR 337914. 1958, as Bridge 1918. 37ft span.

BRIDGE 1951, footbridge, Bridport Road (replaced road bridge 1957). GR 338921. Brick piers, steel stairs and span.

BRIDGE 1952, underbridge, Silver Street, GR 339924. 1932, plate girder, two main girders, cross girders and railbearers. Cantilevered plate parapets. 52ft span (65ft on skew).

SILVER STREET

New Booking Office and canopy 1985/6. New brick stairways 1985/6. Three bays only of 1872 up platform canopy, valancing straightened 1958. Up platform shelter c.2000. (Photos pp. 228/229/236/239/242).

[Up platform 1872 buildings demolished 1985. Down platform 1872 canopy demolished c.1970. Rest of up platform canopy demolished c.2000].

BRIDGE 1954, underbridge, Pymmes Brook, GR 339925. 30ft brick arch.

BRIDGE 1956, underbridge, Park Road (formerly Hyde Road), GR 340928. 1998, as Bridge 1939.

BRIDGE 1957, underbridge, footpath, GR 342933. 1871, stock brick, segmental arch, 13ft span. (Photo p.207).

BRIDGE 1958, underbridge, Bridge Road (now footpath), GR 342934. 1871, stock brick, segmental arch, 16ft span. (Photo p.207).

EDMONTON / LOWER EDMONTON / EDMONTON GREEN

Booking Office building at street level 1978. Lift towers 2014. Covered stairways and waiting rooms above down side stairway 1872. Up platform building 1872. Full lengths of both 1872 platform canopies, new roofing 1978. (Photos pp. 224/226/227/236/237/244).

BRIDGE 1960, underbridge, Church Street, GR 343936. 1998, as Bridge 1939.

BRIDGE 1962, underbridge, Salmon's Brook, GR 342940. 1871, stock

Rectory Road is the most attractive of the new station buildings of the 1975-85 period, perhaps assisted by the retention of the 1958 footbridge section.

The Station Master's house at White Hart Lane is an unlikely survivor. The style, and the lack of any reference in the minutes, suggest that it was not GER-built.

Hackney Downs bears the mark of the quadrupling most notably, as the Up Fast and centre island platforms were wholly new, and in the normal manner of the time received extensive buildings and canopies. This is the Up Fast platform in August 1983, when the original roofing had just been removed (as also on the island platform), enabling other details to be seen better. All work above platform level was in Ashbee's red brick. The 'standard' canopy has longitudinal and transverse RSJs, and aberrant double-curved solid longitudinal brackets.

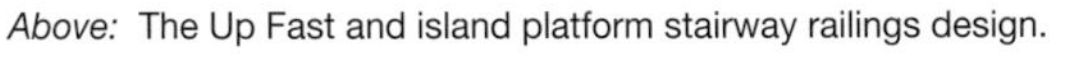

Above: The Up Fast and island platform stairway railings design.

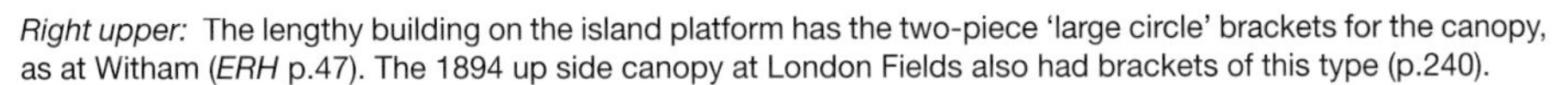

Right upper: The lengthy building on the island platform has the two-piece 'large circle' brackets for the canopy, as at Witham (*ERH* p.47). The 1894 up side canopy at London Fields also had brackets of this type (p.240).

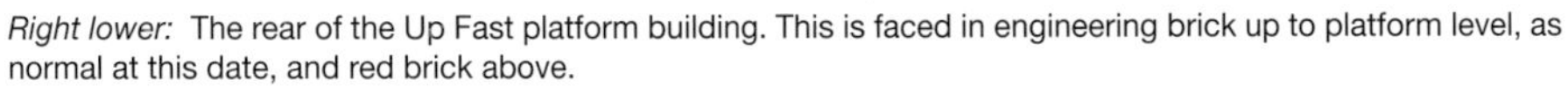

Right lower: The rear of the Up Fast platform building. This is faced in engineering brick up to platform level, as normal at this date, and red brick above.

At Cambridge Heath (as well as London Fields) the 1872 up platform buildings had to be replaced to make room for the quadrupling. The new red brick buildings were in the same style as used at Hackney Downs. The scars of the retained 1872 canopy are evident here. The full length of the rear wall was new, in red brick, in 1894. *Now demolished*. For the 1894 street level building see p.274. *J.E. Connor*

Turning now to the many underbridges reconstructed in the pre-electrification works in 1957/8, the most common type, found at Bridges 1350 1355 and 1356 (Suburban lines), 1915, 1918, 1927, 1937, 1942, 1945, 1946, 1947 and 1950, was the BR standard 'C' type, with three welded steel plate girders and concrete flooring (which hides the cross girders). Almost identical is the 1959 Bridge 1354 (Suburban lines).

A more strikingly modern 1959 reconstruction was effected at Seven Sisters Road, with two single-track welded steel box girder deck span bridges. This type is only possible where the railway is at above average height above the roadway.

Another very modern design was adopted in 1959 at Graham Road (Bridge 1367), with four single-track bridges all in welded steel. The abutments here are wholly 1871, being part of the original four-track section.

Above: St Loy's Road (Bridge 1939) illustrates the BR standard design used for a programme of underbridge reconstruction in 1998, the others being Bridges 1934, 1943, 1944, 1956 and 1960. These are arranged as two single-track bridges. The outer concrete beams are separate, as a bridge strike protection. Here there is also a concrete extension of the Bruce Grove down platform.

The 'prototype' when new – Hoe Street some time in 1871/2, with the trackbed prepared for the laying of the down line. The Hoe Street and St James Street canopies do not have the swept-up ends that all the 1872 stations' canopies have, instead there is a shorter 2ft overhang with the valancing horizontal. The up platform canopy here is unusually wide, 37 boards or 18ft 6in. The down platform / canopy are only 13ft wide.

The photograph clearly shows two different canopy roofing materials; the upper part is glazed, as can be seen from the six areas of light on the ballast. *J.E. Connor collection*

FEATURE: THE 1872 STYLE STATIONS

There were sixteen stations of this type, designed by the GER's Consulting Engineers Edward Wilson & Co for the company's 1864 Act 'Metropolitan' lines. Save for the two 1870 prototypes Hoe Street and St James Street, they were highly standardised in their architectural details, and also as far as possible in plan, but necessarily differing on that front according to whether the line was on viaduct or in cutting, and according to the space available at street level. The style is in spirit the same 'early Gothic' as used at Liverpool Street, with pointed arches (but not the Liverpool Street 'lancets'), and all in stock brick. The ridge-and-furrow platform canopies were a new development for the GER.

THE SURVIVING 1870s STRUCTURES

(excluding the viaducts for the platforms at the elevated stations; and the subways, which were all modernised in the 1970s/80s).

Station	Date	Surviving structures
Bethnal Green	1872	Lower portion only of Down Suburban platform building
Cambridge Heath	1872	Down side covered stairway with waiting rooms above
London Fields	1872	Nil
Hackney Downs	1872	Down platform canopy and building, down side covered stairway with waiting rooms above
Rectory Road	1872	Lower portion only of Booking Office building
Stoke Newington	1872	Stairways minus coverings (also platform retaining walls)
Stamford Hill	1872	Booking Office building and covered footbridge
Seven Sisters	1872	Nil
Bruce Grove	1872	Booking Office building, stairways minus coverings, up platform building, up platform canopy (reduced/reroofed)
White Hart Lane	1872	Up platform building and canopy (reroofed), down platform canopy (reduced/reroofed)
Silver Street	1872	Up platform canopy (reduced)
Lower Edmonton	1872	Covered stairways, up platform building and canopy (reroofed), down platform canopy (reroofed) and waiting rooms above stairway
Clapton	1872	Booking Office building and up platform covered stairs, up platform building and canopy
St James Street	1870/1873/1875	Stairways minus coverings, bases only of up and down platform buildings
Hoe Street	1870/1873	Main up side building, up platform canopy, down platform canopy (reduced)
Wood Street	1873	Stairways minus coverings, base only of up platform building

No station survives fully intact, however Lower Edmonton (where it was originally planned to remove all existing structures in 1976) is intact except for the Booking Office building, and Hoe Street (which has remained in a time warp since 1968) retains the majority of its 1870 structures.

THE 1870 PROTOTYPE STATIONS

Hoe Street (and St James Street), designed in 1869 and part-built in 1869/70, were the prototypes for the many other stations on the 'Metropolitan' lines that followed in 1872. The details of the main buildings are more elaborate than at the 1872 stations, and the canopies are constructed in a different manner.

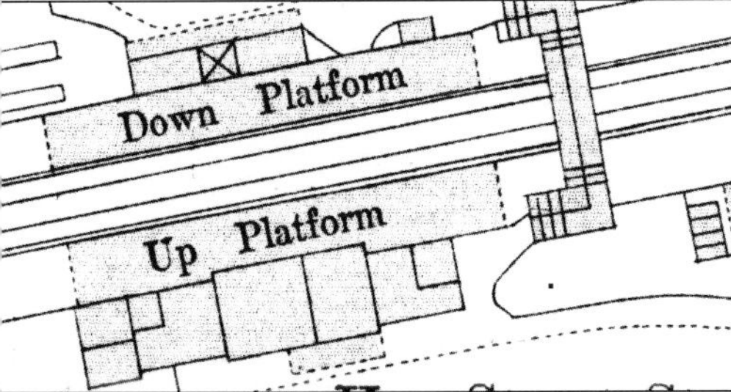

Hoe Street 1894 OS. This was the only station on these lines built at ground level, and thus also differed considerably in *plan* from the other stations, having a large main building on the up side instead of a small BO building at street level and separate platform buildings. This main building of 1869/70 has survived largely unchanged to the present day. The wider central section containing the BO and Booking Hall originally had a modest roadside canopy, details of which are unknown as it was replaced by the smaller timber canopy seen in the photo p.220. The Gents (now demolished) was in a separate block some distance away, an early custom that had been abandoned by 1872 in favour of an integral Gents at the far end of the main platform buildings. The up platform canopy is seen here at its original six-bay length, as it exists again today following the removal in 1967 of the 1907 western extension. The down platform was built in 1873 when the line was doubled and had a canopy of the same six-bay length, and a small staff rooms etc block behind (demolished 1967/8, however the platform rear wall remains). The footbridge was provided in 1887 and removed in 1976.

Detail of Hoe Street exterior. The building is mainly in stock brick, but features stone 'imposts' and 'keystones', and polychromatic (red/stock/blue) brickwork, in the window and door arches, setting it apart from the unrelieved stock brick of the 1872 stations (back cover colour photo). These features are also found in the up side *platform side* openings, although scarcely noticeable owing to the accumulation of dirt! (They are *not* found in the 1873 down side work). The brickwork of the eaves cornice is also not as at the 1872 stations, being all red brick, except for the 'modillions' which are single pieces of terracotta (as used *at corners only* in 1872).

NOTES ON THE OS EXTRACTS

These are all from the 1:1056 maps, reproduced at an approx. scale of 1.3in = 100ft. OS policy on what details to show on these maps changed over the years (and had the 1894 draughtsmen confused!).

The **1872** editions (which exist for Bethnal Green and Cambridge Heath only) *show*

The full internal layout of street level and (where shown) platform level buildings, including door and window openings (stations being classed as 'public buildings' on this front).

The full length of all stairways (omitting platform level buildings above them).

Canopy columns.

They do not show

Subways and stairway railings.

The **1894** editions *show*

Basic internal layout only of street level and platform level buildings. In *some* cases the timber Booking Office structure within the Booking Hall is shown.

Subways.

Stairway central dividing railings.

They do not show

Portions of stairways which have buildings above them (Bethnal Green, Cambridge Heath, London Fields, Hackney Downs, Seven Sisters, White Hart Lane). But in other cases the draughtsman seems to have forgotten this policy and has shown the full stairway and not the waiting rooms / B.O. building above (Rectory Road, Stamford Hill, Bruce Grove, Silver Street, Lower Edmonton, Clapton, Wood Street).

Canopy columns.

Hoe Street exterio c.1960, with th replacement sma canopy over th entrance doorwa only.
Geoff Pembe

Below left: Hoe Street looking east, c.1965, showing the station as it existed in its 'final' form from 1907 to 1967, with the four extra bays at this end of the up side canopy. Th rear wall had been extended in stock brick in 1907 and finished off in correct 1870 style, probably re-using the stonework from the original end point.

Below right: The same view in 1967/8, just after both canopies had been shortened at the west end (by two bays on the down side and four on the up). This work ha temporarily exposed the transverse lattice girders at the new end points. These lattice girders were used in the Hoe Street and St James Street canopies in lieu of the larg decorative brackets at the 1872 stations.
Both: J.E. Conno

Left: This recent view of the Hoe Street up platform canopy, where the original roofing remains, shows how the whole arrangement for carrying the roofing is different here from the 1872 stations' canopies (for which see photos pp. 243 bot / 244 top). Instead of a single longitudinal arched member between columns, here there are four iron 'rafters' between the lattice girders, and one transverse 'purlin' on each side (*cf* two at the 1872 stations) carrying the roof timbers. The Hoe Street down side canopy in 1873 replicated this 1870 construction. No detailed photographs are known of the St James Street canopies prior to their removal, and it has to be *assumed* from the presence of the transverse lattice girders that other details were also as Hoe Street.

Right: Close view of the Hoe Street capitals, which are very similar (but not quite identical) to those at the 1872 stations.

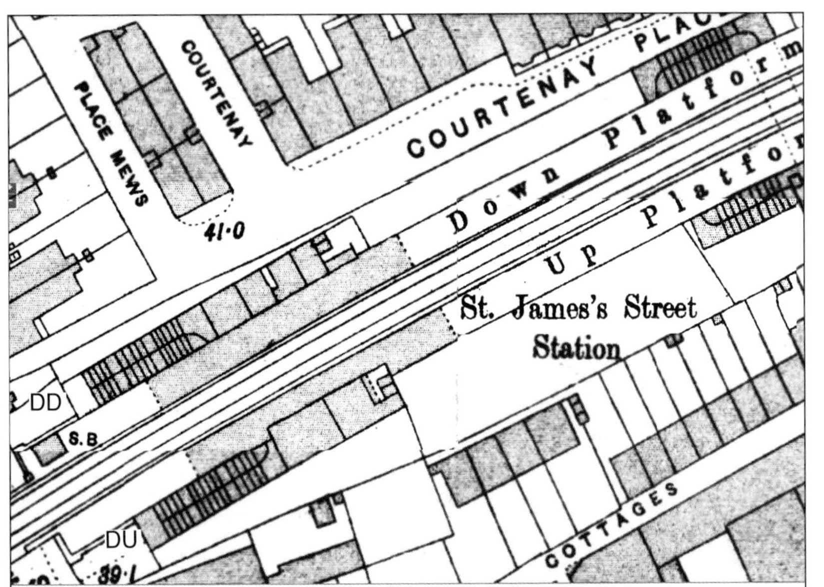

St James Street 1894 OS. The Booking Hall 'building', under the line immediately east of the St James Street road bridge, must date from 1870, as its walls carry the girders on which the line is supported. As at Hoe Street, there was originally only one (the later up) platform. (There are no very early photographs of St James Street to *prove* that this was the permanent structures rather than a temporary timber platform). The down platform was 1873 for doubling, as at Hoe Street, but the down platform building was an afterthought in 1875. The platforms here were built on viaducts. In 1890 a second Booking Office / entrance (just off extract) was provided at the east end with covered stairways to each platform.

In 1895, just after this OS survey, the up platform canopy was extended east to this new entrance. In 1901 the road under the St James Street bridge was widened and a new longer bridge provided, for which several feet had to be shaved off the west side of the Booking Hall 'building', causing a major rearrangement of it, which was in any case desirable because of the huge numbers of passengers being handled here by that date.

The underline Booking Hall resulted in the up and down stairways being in line with each other, unlike all the other 'viaduct' stations. The original separate exit doors of 1872 are marked DU/DD. In the 1901 alterations, the lower parts of both stairways were rearranged; the up side exit door was abolished, and a replacement down side exit door was provided.

The internal details of the up platform building are not shown properly by the OS for some reason.

Left: At St James Street the details of the window and door arches of the street level Booking Hall building are as per Hoe Street, except that the arches are wholly in red brick, not polychromatic. The majority of the present window/door openings are actually 1901 and not 1870 (the only likely exception being the north side street entrance doorway seen here). However it is probable that the original stonework was reused in 1901; plus it is highly unlikely that such features would have been adopted in 1901 if they had not been present previously.

The photograph was taken in 1973 to record the station prior to the 1974/5 reductions. The Station Cafe at left (since made a shop) was the exit lobby at the bottom of the 1901 down side stairs. The wooden office building at left (since removed) was railway-owned.

Above is the small 1873 signal box (lamp room after 1899, now demolished) which had the same '1870' pattern window arches. No close enough photographs are known of the platform buildings to prove that they were / were not in this style.

Left: The three-ring segmental arches of the 1873 St James Street down platform. The *line* however is on embankment (east of the Booking Hall 'bridge').

Above: Looking west at St James Street c.1968. Everything seen here was demolished in 1974. After its eastward extension in 1895, the up platform canopy here was the longest of all the canopies at this type, at around 275ft. The unique single-bay canopy opposite, over the head of the eastern B.O. down side stairs, was added in 1898.

J.E. Connor

Left: The 1873 down platform canopy (demolished 1974), in the 1960s, with the bottom of the valancing cut back a little c.1958 for electrification. As noted opposite the St James Street canopies, on both platforms, were in the Hoe Street style.

J.E. Connor collection

1872 'VIADUCT' STATIONS WITH STREET LEVEL BOOKING OFFICE BUILDINGS

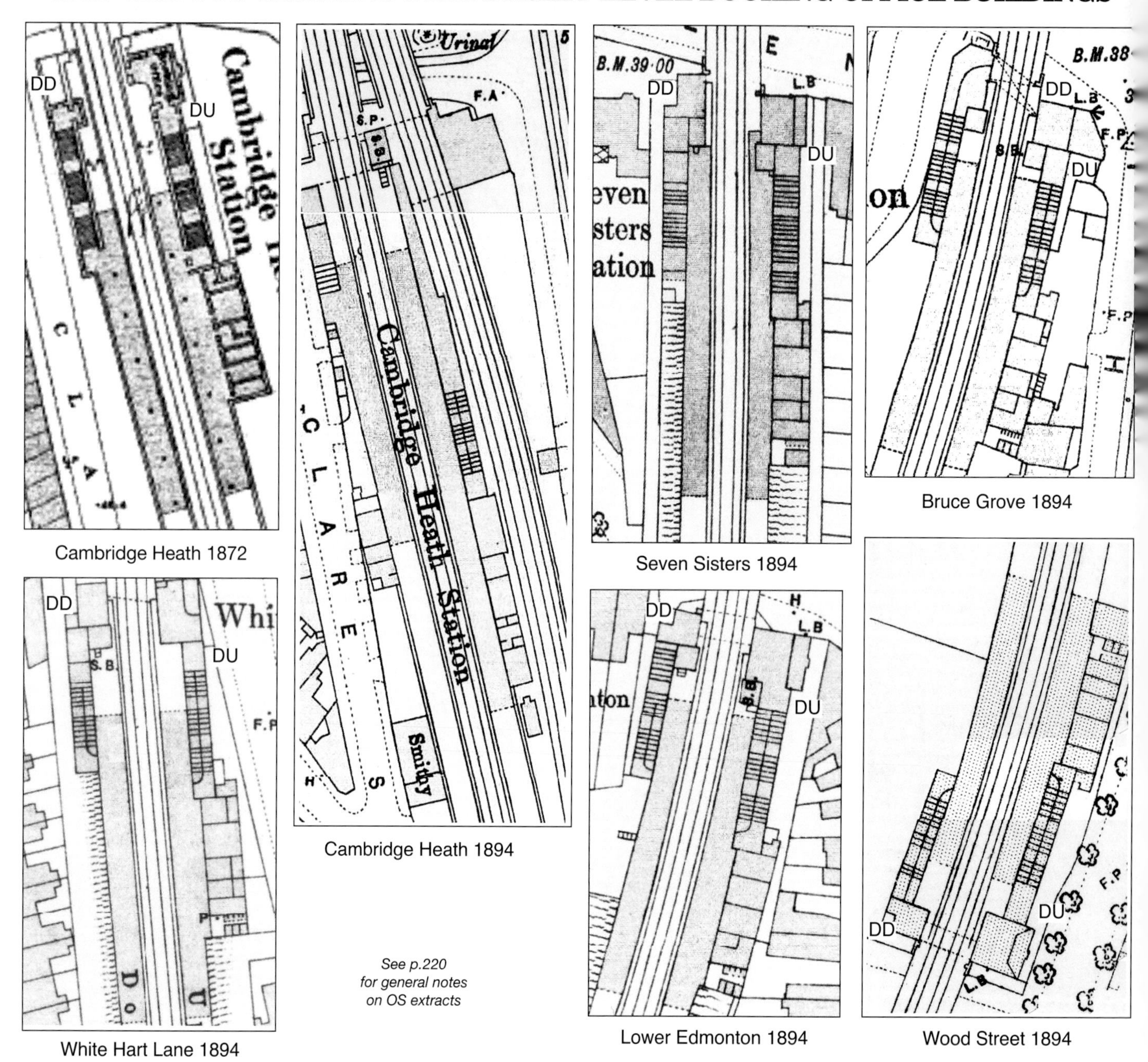

Cambridge Heath 1872

Cambridge Heath 1894

Seven Sisters 1894

Bruce Grove 1894

White Hart Lane 1894

See p.220 for general notes on OS extracts

Lower Edmonton 1894

Wood Street 1894

Five of these stations – Cambridge Heath (in its original state), Seven Sisters, Bruce Grove, White Hart Lane, and Lower Edmonton – were very similar in plan, with the Booking Office building adjacent to the road underbridge at the country end of the up platform. Wood Street and Silver Street were conversely arranged, with the platforms *north* of the road bridges and in consequence the Booking Office at the *London* end of the up platform. (As it had some aberrant features, Silver Street is dealt with separately at p.228; also the other non-standard viaduct stations Bethnal Green, London Fields, and Hackney Downs are discussed separately at pp.230-232).

At Seven Sisters, Bruce Grove, White Hart Lane, Silver Street, Lower Edmonton and Wood Street the line is on embankment and only the platforms are entirely on arches (20, 21, 22, 15, 22 and nk arches respectively). (Bruce Grove had been intended to be wholly on viaduct in the 1863 Deposited Plans and a Board of Trade certificate had to be obtained in 1871 to alter it to embankment). At Bethnal Green / Cambridge Heath / London Fields / Hackney Downs the line is of course on *continuous* viaduct throughout but again the separate higher arches either side for the platforms are evident (photos pp. 206/207).

In each case, there is a subway between the west side of the Booking Hall and the down side stairway, which commences some way to the north (south, at Wood Street) of the up side stairway, as the latter is preceded by a ground level 'bottom landing' area, under a section of gabled roof with the up side exit doorway. The up and down side exit doorways are annotated DU/DD on each map. These exit doorways would only have been manned when a train arrived. Those on the *up* side seem to have passed out of use at an early date, no doubt due to the much smaller numbers of alighting up passengers; in some cases (White Hart Lane, p.224) they were blocked by subsequent structures. The *down* side exits had a much longer life thanks to the large numbers off down evening peak trains, but all have been disused since the end of regular ticket examination. Bruce Grove was unusual in that the down exit door was on the up side (photo p.224), accessed via the subway; the others were all at the foot of the stairs on the down side (photo p.227 top right). The original subways are still in use (except at Seven Sisters and Silver Street), but all modernised in the 1970s/80s.

The stairways were all of three flights, with a gable over each intermediate landing as well as the top and bottom landings.

The platform buildings behind the up platforms, all located immediately south of the head of the stairs, were very standardised, comprising (from the north end - the south end at Silver St / Wood St):

Ladies Waiting Room / General Waiting Room / Staff Room / SM's Office / Lamp Room / Gents.

(The 1894 OS shows partly-different room arrangements at Bruce Grove and Lower Edmonton, also at the 'cutting' stations Rectory Road and Stamford Hill (p.232). But the doors and windows on the platform side, where photos exist, were in the usual positions, so these may have ben subsequent internal alterations only).

At all these stations there was also a short General Waiting Room / Ladies Waiting Room block at the end of the down platform, above the stairs. Oddly, these were beyond the canopy area. It is not *certain* that all of these were 1872 – the Land & Construction Committee decided in September 1870 that 'no waiting rooms be placed on the down side beyond Dalston Junction' [Hackney Downs] - however nothing has been found in the minutes regarding *subsequent* provision. (See also the 1894 map notes on p.220).

The canopies (all originally the *same* length on both platforms, and ending in line with each other) extended from some way north of the head of the up platform stairs, to a short distance beyond the south end of the up side Gents.

This 1950s plan of Seven Sisters shows a standard up platform block still in its original state and each room retaining its original uses. Also the standard down side waiting rooms block above the stairs. (the Left Luggage Office and down side Gents were later provisions).

Total length of up platform building including Gents 72ft.

To save space the various buildings are not *shown the correct distances apart.*

SCALE 25 feet = 1 inch.

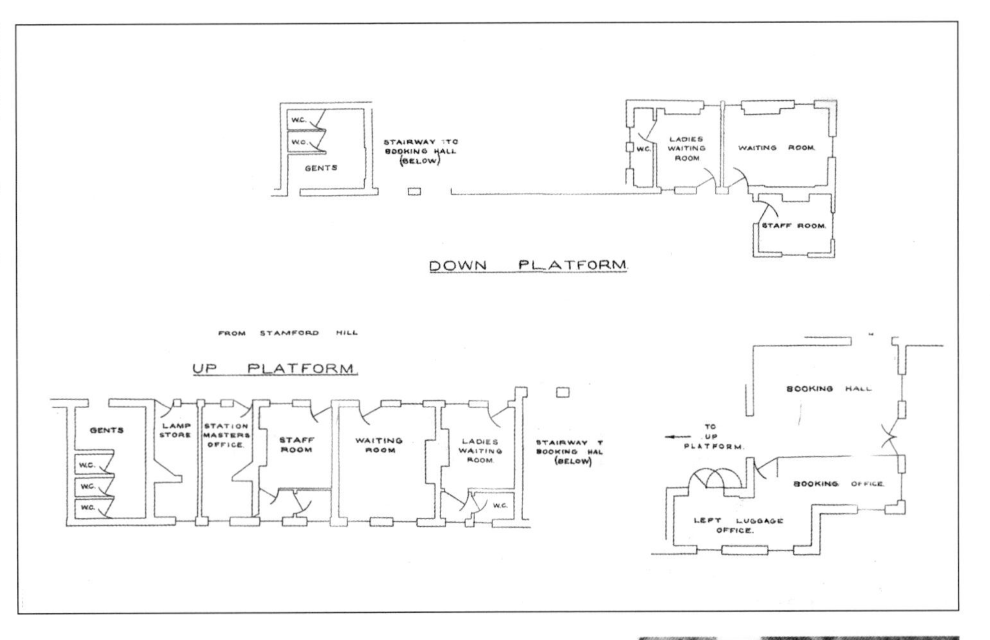

Right: Cambridge Heath down side exterior in 1977, unaltered since 1872. Note how the outline of the stairs is reflected in the exterior brickwork, which is also multiply 'panelled'. The upper intermediate landing has the usual gable, but the lower intermediate landing is below the waiting rooms with their two chimneys. Not surprisingly, no photographs have come to light of the Cambridge Heath *up* side in its pre-1894 form. *Graham Creighton, courtesy Dave Taylor*

Bottom right: The view from the north end in 2014, little changed since 1977, save for some of the windows having been bricked up in 1986, only those lighting the stairway being left glazed. At bottom left (covered in posters) is the former down side exit doorway. Note the several very lengthy drainpipes each with a 'GER 1870' drainpipe head.

Bottom left: Closer view of the upper part of the stairway, showing brickwork details.

Right: A close view of one of the Cambridge Heath drainpipe heads. A good number survive here and at London Fields, and a few in viaduct piers elsewhere, but none are known at the other 1872 stations. They would not have been *installed* in 1870.

Below: Cambridge Heath also has one of them inside the down side stairway.

The Booking Halls / Offices at the 1872 stations were somewhat on the small side for the numbers of passengers using them by the 1890s, and some were in very constrained street situations too. This is Lower Edmonton seen in 1978 shortly before demolition. The section at left with the lower cornice was a 1900 extension, the join in the brickwork being readily seen.

George Hart

The original portion of the Bruce Grove building in 2014. The doors are to the original 1872 design and are the last survivors (although they were originally to have been replaced in the 1976 improvements). The down side exit doorway is at right.

This 1977 view of Bruce Grove from the east side of the High Road emphasises more the flat-roofed extension of 1888. Above the shoe repair shack at left, the gable over the up side exit doorway is seen.

D.J. Taylor

White Hart Lane Booking Office building in August 1969 (since demolished). No extension was ever required here. The Booking Office chimney has been removed, an advertisement board taking its place. The black-shadowed 1872 signal box looms above. To the left a shed has been erected blocking the up side exit doorway.

The maps show that the 1872-93 Cambridge Heath building was similar to this.

J.E. Connor collection

Interior of White Hart Lane Booking Hall on the same day, looking north. Most of these stations had passimeter offices installed by the LNER. The generally decayed ambience shows why BR management were keen to replace the neglected old structures at these stations when money was available!

J.E. Connor collection

Below right:

Wood Street in 1973, shortly before demolition. Although built a year later under a subsequent contract for the Chingford line, this was entirely in the 1872 stations' style. Original 1873 doors are seen in the up side exit doorway.

J.E. Connor

Bottom left:

Another 1973 view of Wood Street, showing the up platform building. Apart from the stairs, everything seen here was removed in 1974.

Bottom right:

The Seven Sisters building was the same as (the original portions of) Bruce Grove and Lower Edmonton. *Since demolished.*

J.E. Connor

Seven Sisters up platform building in 1977, with the stairway roofing already gone (these stairs being out of use by then). At left, outside the main hipped roof, is the Gents. Then Lamp Room (one window); SM's Office (one window, chimney shared with Staff Room); Staff Room (two windows); General Waiting Room (two windows, chimney shared with Ladies Waiting Room); and Ladies Waiting Room (two windows). The building appears to have cellars except at the left end where there is a large open arch, however no plans have emerged to explain the (on the face of it odd) positions of the lower openings. Ordinary platform viaduct arches at far left. *Since demolished.*

Graham Creighton, courtesy Dave Taylor

A contemporary view of Lower Edmonton up side, showing how identical these platform buildings are. The upper landing of the stairways was gabled, as well as the two intermediate landings and the exit doorway at the bottom landing.

D.J. Taylor collection

White Hart Lane, another 1969 photograph. Note how the hipped roof of the platform building has its eaves well below the high 'panelled' platform rear wall. The lower storey had been converted for industrial use by this date (and is still so used today).

J.E. Connor collection

Above: A recent shot of the Bruce Grove up side platform building. The eaves cornice on these buildings is less elaborate than those of the Booking Office buildings; the 'modillions' are red brick but the rest is ordinary stock brick.

Right: Lower Edmonton down side in the 1970s, featuring the out-of-use down side exit door and the small ground level section of the building for the passageway between the subway and the bottom of the stairs (now removed). Above, to the left of the waiting rooms block at the north end of the down platform, the lower section with modern window was a postwar down side staff room.
D.J. Taylor collection

White Hart Lane down side in 1969 just after the stairway roofing, the waiting rooms block, and most of the platform canopy had been removed. The arrangement had been as at Lower Edmonton, except the old signal box here (since demolished) was still in use as a staff room. *J.E. Connor collection*

A close study of the standard 'gothic' coping stonework found on the pillars at the ends of the high portions of platform walls (see the r/h side of the Hoe Street photo at p.220 middle left).

Lower Edmonton up platform, 3-ring segmental arched viaduct.

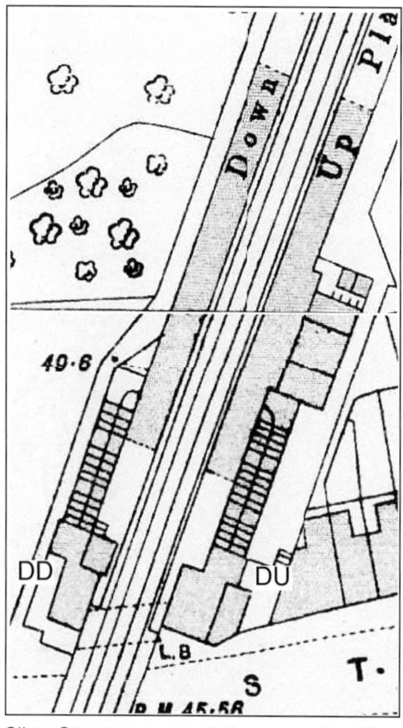

Silver Street was essentially arranged as Wood Street, but uniquely had the up platform building split into two sections, the main block having the waiting rooms / toilets, with the staff rooms in a separate small hipped-roof block over the bottom flight of the stairs, contiguous with the Booking Office building. This block is not shown on the 1894 OS here, the stairs below again being given priority for mapping purposes. It is not at all evident why this splitting of the building was done, unless there was some problem acquiring land from the field to the north.

Silver Street up side, 1935. The Booking Office building, like the 1872 Cambridge Heath building, and Bethnal Green in its original state, had an angled corner, necessitated in this case by the street geography. The presence of the usual central railings in the up side stairway implies that there must have been an exit doorway under the staff block, however there are no plans or photographs to prove this. If there was, it had ceased to be used by this date, as the route to the street is fully fenced off. The photograph was taken to record the completion in 1933 of the North Circular Road improvements, lowering the roadway and providing a longer bridge. The 'Silver Street Railway Station' sign is unusual. In 1955 the road was further lowered (p.242). *D.J. Taylor collection*

A May 1931 view, taken to record the scene prior to the start of the road works. For the 1872 bridge see p.210. The portion of the building covering the passageway between the subway and the down side stairs is a mirror image of that at Lower Edmonton (p.224). To the left of it, the apex of the arch of the down side exit doorway can just be seen (above the elaborate woodwork of the adjacent non-railway building). The fencing suggests that this door too was out of use. The 1872 signal box above – the only one situated at the *south* end of a platform – still has its (LNER) nameboard here, but in the 1935 photograph above the nameboard is gone, as the box was abolished in the 1934 colour light resignalling. To the left of the box is the usual waiting room block.

D.J. Taylor collection

Looking north through the Silver Street platforms in May 1931.

In later years the frontage had a very gloomy neglected appearance, although the only structural change was the bricking in of the upper part of the entrance doorway. *Since demolished.*

J.E. Connor collection

Silver Street never had a passimeter office, and retained its C19 Booking Hall arrangement until the 1984 fire that brought about the removal of most of the old buildings here. This view looks north-east past the ticket collector's hut to the passage to the up side stairway, with the Booking Office at right.

J.E. Connor collection

The up platform staff rooms block, which contained Porters Room and Lamp Room (right, the latter accessed from the former), and SM's Office (left). *Since demolished.*

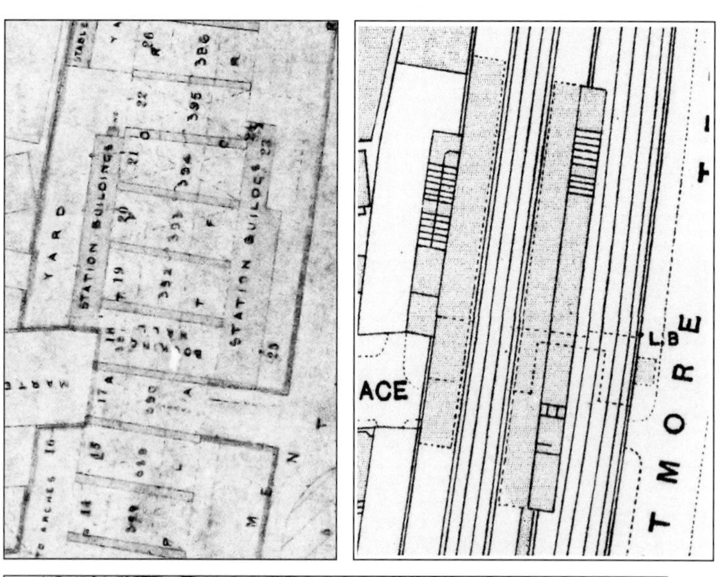

Far left: London Fields in its 1872-94 form as shown in the GER 1887 viaduct plan. It differed in having no Booking Office building - the 1872 B.O. was in the viaduct arch immediately north of the Martello Terrace underbridge. The 1872 up platform building had its platform frontage a few feet to the east of its 1894 successor.

Left: 1894 OS, showing the new up side building. Note the canopy over the new entrance, long since gone and not known from photographs.

The London Fields down side exit doorway at the foot of the stairs, with derelict waiting rooms above (which the OS *does* show here), during the early 1980s closure period. Compare the recent view at p.206. *J.E. Connor*

Bethnal Green 1872 OS. This was the only 1872 style station with four platforms, and therefore the only one with a wide island platform canopy supported on two rows of columns. The Booking Office building is shown in its original form. The three stairways are shown in full, but the subway and the down side platform building are omitted. Until 1891 there were only four tracks through the station (Local and Main lines). The Up Main platform rear wall was the south side of the viaduct.

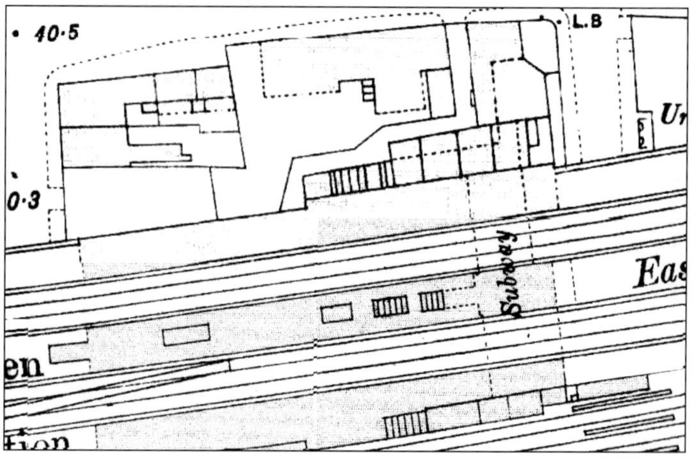

Bethnal Green 1894 OS. The Booking Office extension of 1887 is shown. The two pairs of lines serving the platforms were now Suburban and Local, the new Through lines to the south passing behind the Up Local (as it now was) platform wall. Otherwise the station was still as in 1872, but the OS *shows* things differently. The main platform building behind the Down Suburban platform (appropriately so located, given that so many of the passengers here were boarding *down* trains) is shown in full, as is the smaller block behind the Up Local platform, and the subway; but most of the stairways are now omitted.

The station frontage in the 1950s, Tapp Street underbridge at left. The northernmost part of the 1887 Booking Office extension had been removed for road widening by this date. Behind the original portion of the B.O. was a storeroom (two windows), with the Gents above it. This down platform building was laid out to the standard pattern used for *up* platform buildings elsewhere (although the OS omits the wall between the SM's Office and the Lamp Room). *Now largely demolished.* *D.J. Taylor collection*

The western half of the Bethnal Green frontage, photographed in June 1984 shortly before demolition. The ground level doorway facing us was almost certainly the original passenger exit doorway – the OS maps (when studied in combination) show that it was accessible from all platforms, and also there was a pathway from it to the street. The original doors were still in place. (The lower half of this building still exists, with the door and the windows blocked up).

The west side wall of the B.O. building (left) is, oddly, still standing in 2014. *D.J. Taylor*

Below left: One bay of the Down Suburban canopy, with Ladies Waiting Room door and window at right. The 27ft long canopy bays here were the longest at any of the '1872' stations (see p.238). *D.J. Taylor*

Below: Because the stairways at a standard 1872 style station were outside of the platform rear walls, the only stairwell protection railings on an 1872 station platform were these on the Bethnal Green island platform. They had elaborately decorative ironwork, seen here casting shadows in winter sunlight. *Since removed.* *J.E. Connor*

Above: Looking west along the Bethnal Green Down Suburban platform around 1962, prior to the canopies being reduced in length and the decline in the general ambience. The Up Local platform had been removed in 1946 to facilitate the realignment of the Through lines, and only Suburban lines trains called after that; however the island platform's face to the Down Local was left for long afterwards. No photographs are known showing the details of the island platform canopy. *All now removed.*

J.E. Connor collection

Right: The Hackney Downs Down Suburban platform buildings and stairway have a fairly well-preserved exterior, but it is only visible at this sharp angle. The arrangement is non-standard, with the Gents at left (as at Bethnal Green), then the waiting rooms with the usual flat roof and two chimneys, and further flat-roofed offices south of the stairway.

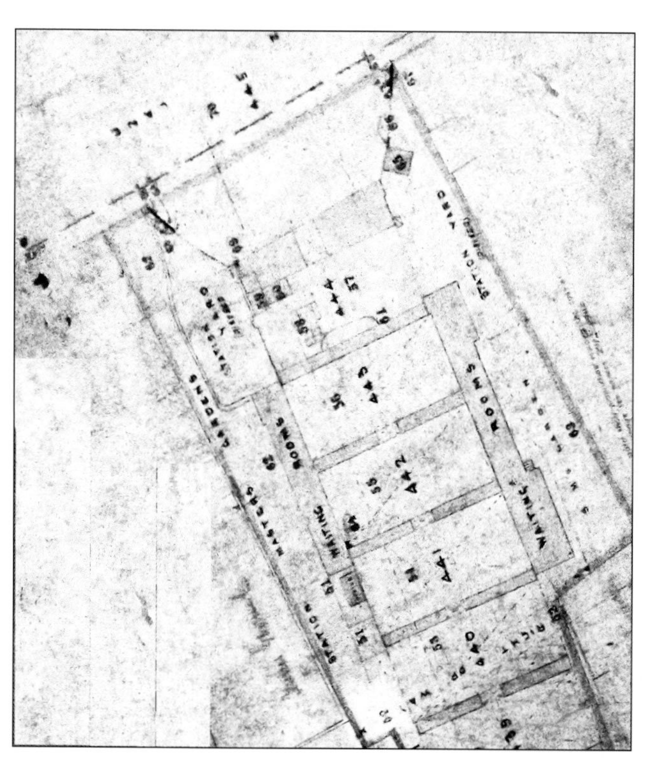

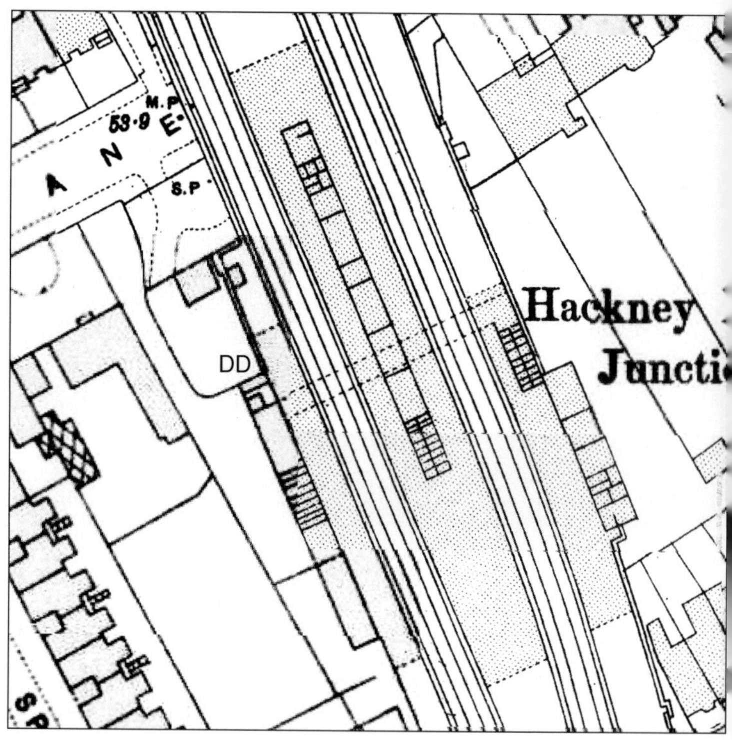

1887 viaduct plan showing Hackney Downs station in its 1872-94 form, including the original up platform building which was demolished in 1893/4. This station differed in having four tracks between the platforms, also the Booking Office was in an arch (444) as at London Fields. The blocks shown as 'Waiting Rooms' included the stairways.

Hackney Downs 1894 OS, just after the 1893/4 reconstruction.

1872 STATIONS IN CUTTING WITH STREET LEVEL BOOKING OFFICE BUILDINGS

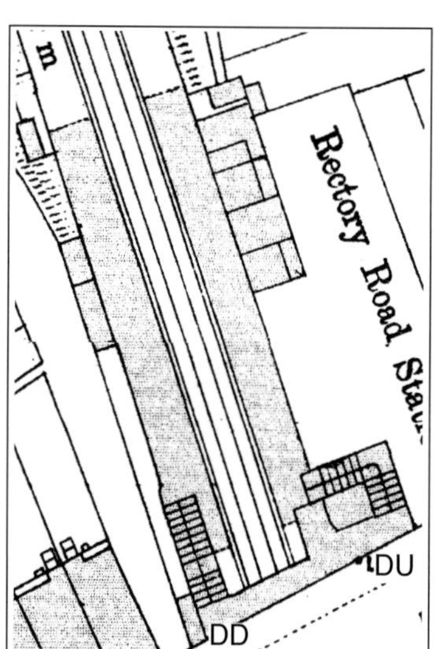

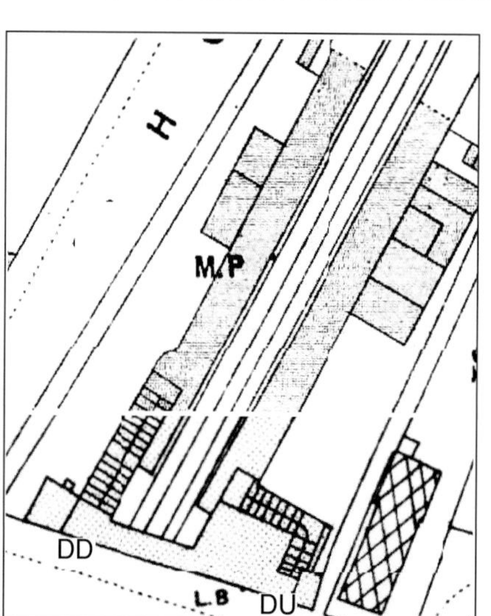

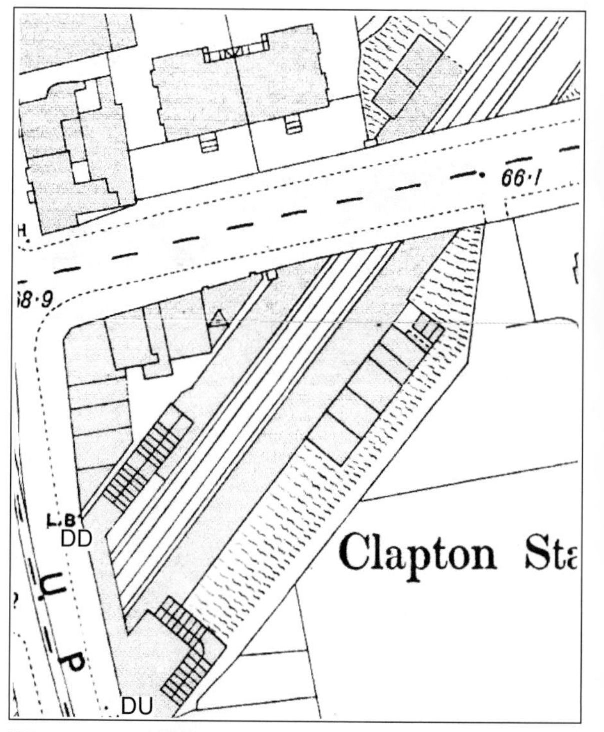

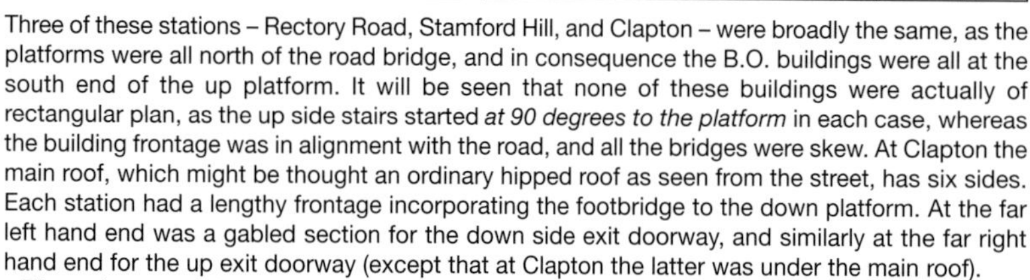

Three of these stations – Rectory Road, Stamford Hill, and Clapton – were broadly the same, as the platforms were all north of the road bridge, and in consequence the B.O. buildings were all at the south end of the up platform. It will be seen that none of these buildings were actually of rectangular plan, as the up side stairs started *at 90 degrees to the platform* in each case, whereas the building frontage was in alignment with the road, and all the bridges were skew. At Clapton the main roof, which might be thought an ordinary hipped roof as seen from the street, has six sides. Each station had a lengthy frontage incorporating the footbridge to the down platform. At the far left hand end was a gabled section for the down side exit doorway, and similarly at the far right hand end for the up exit doorway (except that at Clapton the latter was under the main roof).

The stairways at these three stations had two flights (instead of the three flights at the viaduct stations). The down side stairway was straight, but the up side stairs had a lower flight running partly through the bottom of the rear section of the main building, then a 90 degree turn at the landing, with the upper flight running alongside the east wall of the main building.

The up platform buildings, 'handed' the same way as Wood Street, were of course largely invisible except on the platform side. They were a good way down the platform from the stairways, and the Gents at the far end was right at the north end of the canopy.

As at the 'viaduct' stations, the canopies (Clapton excepted) were the same length on both platforms, and ended in line with each other.

Behind the down platform, at Rectory Road and Stamford Hill, was a small Waiting Room / Ladies Waiting Room block, equivalent to those at the north ends of the down platform at the viaduct stations. These however were wholly or partly additions of c.1880. At Clapton the down side waiting rooms, provided in 1881, had to be erected beyond the Southwold Road overbridge, as the portion of the platform up to the bridge had a retaining wall behind.

Right (two photographs): Details of the cornice on the 1872 Booking Office buildings (this was identical at *all* the 1872 stations). Stamford Hill (p.233 bottom left) has weathered very well. Clapton (right) shows the single-piece terracotta 'modillions' used at corners, in lieu of the red brick of the others. The course of nailhead (small pyramids) decoration is also in red brick. The curving courses above and below, and the string course at the foot of the modillions, are in a whitish brick.

he best street frontage view of one of these tations in their full glory is this of Stamford Hill .1910, not however in its *original* state as coal offices had been added at each end. Warren & Co's (?) office at left had been provided in 882, Tite's at right was present by 1894. Next o Tite's the up side exit doorway has doors to he standard 1872 design. *J.E. Connor collection*

Below: Stamford Hill in 1977. The Driving School occupies the former coal office, but he down side exit doorway and its gabled oof had been removed altogether. The two windows in the footbridge section were altered; the up side exit doorway has become a window; and Tite's office has been heavily altered. Nevertheless this was the best-preserved station of this type by then. The passimeter office can be seen through the main doorway.

The up side exit doorway and the ex-Tite's shop have since been demolished. *D.J. Taylor*

Left: Stamford Hill Booking Hall looking east, alongside the passimeter office, from the entrance doorway to the head of the up side stairs, 1979. *J.E. Connor collection*

Far left: A recent view along the Stamford Hill covered footbridge, the only remaining example of this type since 1958. The frontage windows have been restored in a more appropriate form since the 1977 photograph, but those on the rear side have been blocked.

Below: Rear of the Stamford Hill building in the late 1970s, after the platform canopies had been shortened and the down side stairway roofing been removed. This photograph serves to show, better than any taken during the years when the full canopies existed, the arrangement of the up side stairs, with the first flight partly within the rear portion of the building (which is slightly lower than the main portion), but the rest of the stairway separately roofed, as at the viaduct stations, alongside the north and east sides of the building.

At Rectory Road the rear portion of the building was smaller, and set back further from the platform edge. Note that the 1894 OS maps do not show these rear portions properly.

No useful views have been found of the Rectory Road frontage prior to the 1972 fire, which left it in the state shown here (in 1976) until the 1984/5 rebuilding. The footbridge section had been rebuilt in 1958, as at Clapton, in connection with the reconstruction of the road bridge. The down side exit doorway survived to the end, as did the up. The little shop at left was definitely not subjected to any appropriate architectural efforts! In 2014 only the footbridge section remains (p.216).

In September 1870 the GER Land & Construction Committee considered this station and resolved:

'Station to be on the level, no road is wanted for cabs or carriages, Engineer to make the station on the most economical plan'. *J.E. Connor collection*

Right: Clapton in its original state, c.1910. The up side exit doorway is out of view to right. There were non-railway properties immediately adjoining at both ends of the frontage here, hence no coal offices / shops appeared.
J.E. Connor collection

Below: The road frontage of Clapton station as altered in 1958 (photograph July 1979). The original covered footbridge had to be taken down when the road bridge was reconstructed in 1958; it was replaced in 1950s style. The unique 'ashlared' rendering-over of the brickwork of the front of the Booking Office building had been done at an earlier date, presumably because of decaying brickwork. The up side exit doorway at right, here within the main part of the building, had long since been converted to a window; it was bricked up in 1985.
J.E. Connor collection

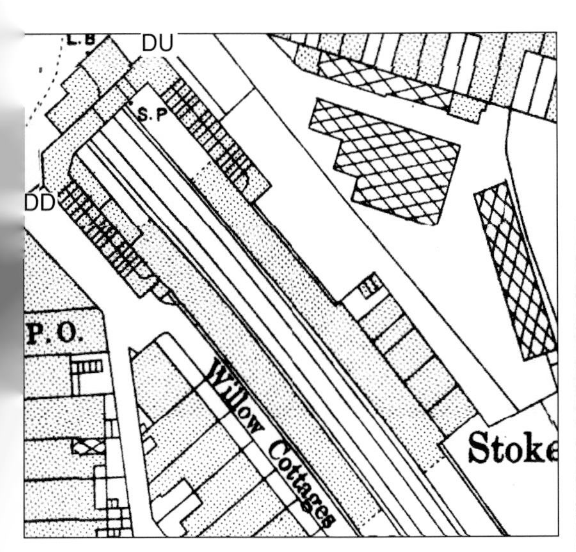

Stoke Newington 1894 OS. This was rather different to all other stations, as the main building was in a large forecourt area above the tunnel (actually an extended cut-and-cover road bridge). A passageway behind the Booking Hall, within the main building, led to the usual covered stairways, which were both straight, and in line with each other. Hence no footbridge was required. The down platform had a retaining wall throughout its length and had no waiting rooms until a narrow (timber?) block was erected alongside the stairway in 1877. However the northern part of the up platform did not have a retaining wall immediately behind, and a standard platform block could be provided here. This was 'handed' the same way round as at the other 'cutting' stations, so, uniquely for an 1872 type station, the Gents was at the end nearest the stairway.

Right and below: These two views looking north along the down platform illustrate well the walled cutting location of this station. The photo at right was taken in November 1958, after the track through the tunnel had been lowered for electrification clearances. The view below is from July 1959, and shows how the up side retaining wall ended at the point where the canopy / platform building began. *Canopies and station building demolished 1974/5.*

D.J. Taylor collection

Stoke Newington in the 1900s, the piers of the forecourt gates conspicuous in the foreground. The usual gabled up side exit doorway is seen at left. The down side exit doorway at far right was angled at 45 degrees.

D.J. Taylor collection

COVERED STAIRWAYS

At the 'viaduct' stations there were two arches leading to the top landing of the stairway, this being necessary initially as passengers were (in theory) to be kept to the in or out sides of the stairs throughout – entry on the side nearest the track, exit on the outside. This is Bruce Grove up side in 1977, with the Ladies Waiting Room still in use at right. *D.J. Taylor*

The Silver Street up side top landing had seating provided latterly; it had no doubt been found that these areas were more sheltered than the platform seats. Photograph 1982.

Correspondingly, there were two arches at the *foot* of the stairway at the 'cutting' stations. Rectory Road down side in 1976. *J.E. Connor collection*

Cambridge Heath down side is aberrant in having a *single* archway at the top, because this stairway had to be built partly into the width of the (majority of the) platform, owing to the street immediately adjacent on the west side restricting the available landtake. The arch was angled (as shown by the OS), because of the platform being wider to the south. This is the only one of the five extant 1872 covered stairways that does *not* retain the original timber roofing. Additionally, the original bottom portion of the stairs has been replaced by a short flight at 90 degrees leading into the subway.

Lower Edmonton up side in 1975 from from the top landing. The centre railings were not required to *wholly prevent* passengers using the 'wrong' side, but merely to encourage a 'keep to the right' policy, to facilitate the situation at busy times. As is evident here, both the exit door and the platform could actually be reached from either side. Even in the earliest years it is unlikely that the exit doorways were manned for every train. The ticket collector could prevent anyone getting *in* that way when they were open. *D.J. Taylor*

Above: Bruce Grove up side stairs, from the top landing, in 1977. The centre railing here had been removed by this date. The Way Out sign at the bottom now directed passengers out through the Booking Hall. *Roofing removed 1981.* *D.J. Taylor*

Left: Rectory Road down side stairway, 1976, from the top landing by the exit doorway. *Demolished c.1980.*

J.E. Connor collection

Above: A recent view of Lower Edmonton down side from the bottom. Looking up like this, we can see the two sections of cross-gabled roof, at each of the intermediate landings, each with four brackets (on corbels) supporting the transverse beams. There are also intermediate beams between landings, similarly bracketed.

Left: London Fields down side, in the closure years. *Demolished 1986.* *J.E. Connor*

Above left: To be different, Hackney Downs down side has *straight* brackets. (The brackets at the other recorded stations are identical, however there are several stations for which no photographs of the stairways are known). The bottom part of this stairway, below the bracket-less transverse beam, must have been heavily altered when the cross-'subway' was altered in 1894.

Right: Rectory Road up side, 1976, looking down from the top landing by the exit door, to the middle landing where the change of direction is made. This is a fine image of the 'gothic' ambience of the 1872 stations, which in some ways was enhanced as they decayed. *Demolished 1984/5.*
J.E. Connor collection

Above right: The middle landing of the similar up side stairway at Clapton, photographed in 2014, with everything now in excellent condition, but with modern railings. In contrast to the bracketed transverse beam at Rectory Road, there is a transverse *girder* above the entrance to the upper flight here. This upward view also shows the gabled roof over the landing.

PLATFORM CANOPIES

Station	Platform	Date	Canopy	Notes
Bethnal Green	Down Suburban	1872	7 bays / 197ft	Reduced by 3 bays at west end 1960s, rest removed 1985
	Island	1872	7 bays / 197ft	Reduced by 3 bays at west end 1960s, rest removed 1985
	Up Local	1872	7 bays / 197ft	Removed with platform 1946
Cambridge Heath	Down Suburban	1872	6 bays / 152ft	Extended by 2 bays / 48ft at north end c.1905. Removed 1960s
	Up Suburban	1872	6 bays / 152ft	Extended by 4 bays / 96ft at south end 1894. Removed c.1980
London Fields	Down Suburban	1872	6 bays / 152ft	Removed c.1985
	Up Suburban	1872	(u) 6 bays / 152ft	Removed 1893/4
Hackney Downs	Down [Suburban]	1872	6 bays / 152ft	Extended by 2 bays / 50ft at south end 1895, bottom straightened 1958, full length remains
	Up	1872	6 bays / 152ft	Removed with platform 1893/4
Rectory Road	Down	1872	6 bays / 152ft	Reduced by 3 bays at north end 1960s, and by one bay at south end c.1978, rest removed 1984/5
	Up	1872	6 bays / 152ft	Removed 1984/5
Stoke Newington	Down	1872	6 bays / 152ft	Removed 1974
	Up	1872	6 bays / 152ft	Removed 1974
Stamford Hill	Down	1872	6 bays / 152ft	Reduced by 3 bays at north end 1970s, rest removed 1984
	Up	1872	6 bays / 152ft	Reduced by 3 bays at south end 1970s, rest removed 1984
Seven Sisters	Down	1872	8 bays / 172ft	Reduced by 3 bays at north end 1970s, rest removed 1984
	Up	1872	8 bays / 172ft	Reduced by 4 bays at north end 1970s, rest removed 1984
Bruce Grove	Down	1872	7 bays / 148ft	Removed 1981
	Up	1872	7 bays / 148ft	Reduced by two bays at north end 1981, rest remains, new roofing 2000
White Hart Lane	Down	1872	7 bays / 148ft	Bottom straightened 1958, reduced by 4 bays at south end 1969, rest remains, new valancing and roofing u1978
	Up	1872	7 bays / 148ft	Bottom straightened 1958, full length remains, new valancing and roofing u1978
Silver Street	Down	1872	7 bays / 148ft	Bottom straightened c.1958, removed c.1970
	Up	1872	7 bays / 148ft	Bottom straightened c.1958, reduced by 4 bays at south end c.2000, rest remains
Lower Edmonton	Down	1872	7 bays / 148ft	Full length remains, new roofing 1978
	Up	1872	7 bays / 148ft	Full length remains, new roofing 1978
Clapton	Down	1872	4.5 bays south of road bridge, 1.5 bays north of road bridge / 175ft (including bridge)	Removed 1970s
	Up	1872	8 bays / 200ft	Full length remains
St James Street	Down	1873	6 bays / 124ft	Removed 1974 [Also separate 1898 one-bay section, removed 1974]
	Up	1870	6 bays / 124ft	Extended by u8 bays / c.160ft at east end 1895, west end removed c.1970, rest removed 1974
Hoe Street	Down	1873	6 bays / 124ft	Reduced by 2 bays / 40ft at west end 1967/8, rest remains
	Up	1870	6 bays / 124ft	Extended by 4 bays / 80ft at west end 1907, this section removed 1967/8, rest remains
Wood Street	Down	1873	7 bays / 148ft	Altered 1950s, removed 1974/5
	Up	1873	7 bays / 148ft	Altered 1950s, removed 1974/5

The following patterns will be evident:

Hoe Street and St James Street had 124ft long 6-bay canopies (20ft between column centres).

On the first section of the Edmonton line, stations Cambridge Heath to Stamford Hill had 152ft long 6-bay canopies (24ft between column centres).

On the second section of the Edmonton line, stations Bruce Grove to Lower Edmonton had 148ft long 7-bay canopies, as did Wood Street (20ft between column centres).

Bethnal Green (27ft between column centres) was non-standard, Seven Sisters was made up of the standard 20ft bays for this section of line, and Clapton of 24ft bays.

See p.244 for views of the different length bays. The most common width is 14ft (28 valancing boards), some are 13ft (26 boards) or otherwise as required.

Hoe Street and St James Street canopies are to a different design, as described at pp. 220/1. As they do not have the 4ft long swept-up sections at each end, the canopy ends only 2ft beyond the last columns rather than 4ft beyond.

All canopy extensions were done in the original style.

Apart from the canopies necessarily removed as part of station rebuildings (Bethnal Green 1946, London Fields 1893/4, Hackney Downs 1893/4), all canopies remained intact until the mid-1960s. There were then piecemeal reductions and removals, followed by many of the remainder being removed in the 1984/5 GLC-funded station improvements.

Another ridge-and-furrow canopy was provided at Bishopsgate Low Level, Up Through platform, in 1875, but no photographs showing the details exist. Subsequent examples appeared (but with different designs of column and bracket) at Coborn Road 1883, Ipswich island platform 1883, Globe Road 1884, and March 1885. These were probably all designed just before the 1883 change of GER engineering responsibilities. Bishopsgate Low Level island platform received a ridge-and-furrow canopy as late as 1903, with different details.

Starting with some general 'atmosphere', *above* is White Hart Lane in October 1954, and *below* Silver Street at the same time. These were by coincidence the two stations where the canopies had to be altered when the track was raised a few years later (pp. 241/2). *J.E. Connor collection*

Cambridge Heath looking north i the early 1960s. After it southward extension by four bay in 1894, the up platform canop here (right) was the secon longest (after St James Stree canopy of this type. There is n actual evidence as to precise what was done here in 1893/4 however the 28 boards in the en valancing show that the canop was still of the standard widt afterwards, so it seems likely tha it remained in situ throughou even though the rear wall had t be rebuilt. *All now removed.*

J.E. Conno collectio

Cambridge Heath looking south. The unusual shaping (for reasons unknown) of the up side canopy at the north end was already so around 1950, not a pre-electrification change.

J.E. Connor collection

At London Fields the 1872 up platform canopy could not be retained or adapted, as the tight space available for the quadrupling here meant that a new up platform building had to be built well forward into the former platform width. Accordingly a new 'standard' canopy was provided, on 'large circle' brackets as at Hackney Downs island platform. This had its valancing cut short in the pre-electrification works, whereas the 1872 down side canopy (right) remained in original condition until both canopies were removed in 1985.

J.E. Connor collection

›p: At Clapton the very skew ›outhwold Road overbridge ›eant that the final bays of the ›anopies at that end were not full ›ays, and that the down side ›anopy was shorter than the up. : left we see how the first bay of ›e canopies at these 'cutting' ›ations was supported on the ›de wall of the stairway (see also ›ectory Road p.243 top). The 'own platform here had a retaining ›all behind. There was a further ›hort section of canopy beyond ›e bridge. *Down side canopy ›nce removed.*

J.E. Connor collection

›iddle: White Hart Lane up side, ›969. The track over the bridge ›vas raised 2ft 9in in 1958 to ›nable ordinary double-decker ›uses to run along White Hart ›ane. In consequence the canopy ›alancing had to be levelled off at ›he bottom. The platforms of ›ourse had to be raised as well, ›nore so at the north end, as can ›e seen by looking at the bases of ›he columns. The whole of this ›anopy survives in 2014 but now ›as new roofing and valancing. ›his is a 13ft wide (26 boards) ›anopy. *J.E. Connor collection*

Bottom: White Hart Lane down side on the same day in 1969. In addition to the 1958 work for the track raising, it had just been 'rationalised', with the removal of the southernmost four bays and the upper parts of the rear wall behind. No new end valancing was provided when these reductions were done, leaving a 'rough edge' which enhanced the sense of decline. This canopy too has since been reroofed and revalanced. In addition to the 1872 signal box surviving as a staff room, a new small shunter's hut had been provided for the goods yard staff. The single arches at the head of the stairways here are a later alteration.

J.E. Connor collection

Left: A second case of levelling off of the valancing was Silver Street. This wa again due to raising of the track and platforms, as can be seen from the base the columns in this 1982 view of the up platform. The 1933 North Circular Roa bridge was raised by 300mm in 1955. Note the railings provided to assi passengers down the new steps into the waiting rooms.

Below: Although the majority of 1872 canopies did not need to be altered at a for electrification clearances – the electrification was at 6.25kV and not 25k throughout these lines – it seems that this *was* necessary at Hackney Down where the valancing was levelled off as at White Hart Lane and Silver Street. (Ther was *no* raising of the track / platform here, as can be seen from the full height c the column bases still being visible). The photograph dates from August 1969 an everything is still the same today. At left the high rear wall, extended southward in 1895 along with the canopy, was finished off in correct 1872 style.

The St James Street canopies were also altered, to a lesser extent (p.221).

J.E. Connor collectio

The Wood Street canopies were altered to this form some time around the early 1950s (a 1930s photograph shows the valancing still in its original state). The cause is not known. Both canopies were removed in the 1974/5 work here.

J.E. Connor collection

As the 1970s advanced, the number of shortened and decaying canopies increased. *Right* is Stamford Hill up side in 1979, *left* Rectory Road down side in 1976. As one would expect, more down side canopies than up side were reduced in length. *Both canopies since removed entirely*. *J.E. Connor collection*

Rectory Road down side later became the very epitome of decay, reduced to two bays of which only one was actually intact! – as seen here in September 1982. However the whole of the up side canopy was still present at this date, remaining until the 1984/5 alterations here.

Bruce Grove in summer 1984. The down platform canopy had been removed altogether in 1981, and the small brick shelter provided in lieu, and the rear wall reduced in height. At the north end of the down platform is a small postwar staff room like that at Lower Edmonton (p.227 top).

Clapton up side in the 1970s, highlighting the original standard 1872 canopy roofing arrangements, which now remain only here and at Hackney Downs (and the remaining three bays at Silver Street). The longitudinal brackets are extended as an arch which carries one apex beam and two intermediate 'purlins' on each side of the bay. (For the different style of roofing at the 1870 stations, see p.220). This is the southwest end of the up platform building, the doors still plated as Waiting Room and Ladies Waiting Room, but both out of use, another contribution to the sense of decay in these years.

J.E. Connor collection

A close view of '1872' brackets and capitals. These are wholly standardised. The brackets are entirely in the same vein as the larger brackets in the Liverpool Street roof. Seven Sisters, 1982.

Detail of 1872 style valancing (Bruce Grove up side, 1984). Each board is 6in wide.

Right: These photographs illustrate how the different bay lengths found on the different sections of the lines (as tabulated at p.238), are reflected visually.

Upper – Hoe Street down platform, 20ft between column centres, 40 valancing boards per bay.

Middle – Rectory Road, 24ft between column centres, 48 valancing boards per bay.

Bottom – Lower Edmonton, 20ft between column centres, 40 valancing boards per bay.

(See also Bethnal Green at p.231 – 27ft between column centres, 54 valancing boards per bay).

A close study of the Rectory Road view will show that whereas on the r/h side there were (as in most cases) two boards at equal height at the bottom of the V, on the l/h side one board is lower than the others!

Lower Edmonton, showing the new roofing installed here and at White Hart Lane c.1978. The brackets show the effect of overmuch paint!

The new section of '1872' style canopy installed at Bruce Grove (down platform) in 2000. This includes a new stock brick rear wall with 1872 type double archway.

1872 SIGNAL BOXES

All these are now demolished, but they must be covered as they were a significant part of the '1872' theme. They were provided only t the 'viaduct' stations Seven Sisters to Lower Edmonton (and probably also at Cambridge Heath and London Fields, where the original oxes were replaced in 1894 and no photographs are known). McKenzie & Holland had the signalling contract for the whole of these lines, nd standard McK&H Type 1 boxes were provided elsewhere.

It was very rare in this country for signal boxes to be designed to match station buildings, and only happened on new lines. This was ne of the most significant cases.

They were all abolished under the 1934 colour light resignalling, but most found new uses as staff rooms etc, and White Hart Lane nd Silver Street lasted into the 1970s.

(See also White Hart Lane at pp. 227/241, and the St James Street box at p.221).

he best photograph of any of these boxes is the Silver Street 1931 official, here nlarged. The boxes were 12ft square, built in the usual 1872 stock brick, with three arrow pointed-arch windows on the front and the non-door end, one window and oor at the door end. Note the *casement* opening window at the front corner. The aves cornice was in the same vein as on the Booking Office buildings, with the red rick 'modillions'.

D.J. Taylor collection

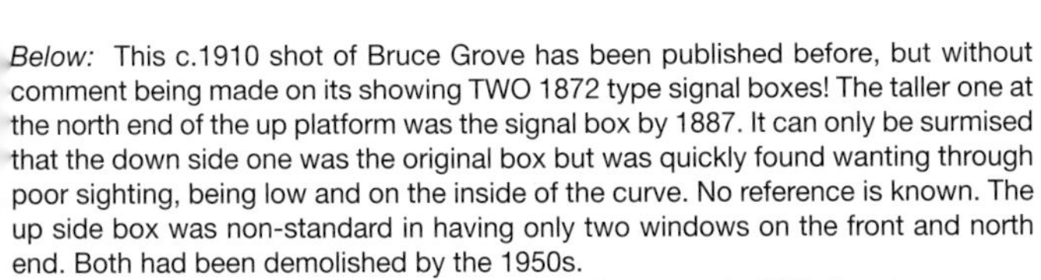

Below: This c.1910 shot of Bruce Grove has been published before, but without comment being made on its showing TWO 1872 type signal boxes! The taller one at the north end of the up platform was the signal box by 1887. It can only be surmised that the down side one was the original box but was quickly found wanting through poor sighting, being low and on the inside of the curve. No reference is known. The up side box was non-standard in having only two windows on the front and north end. Both had been demolished by the 1950s.

The 1894 maps of Seven Sisters and Lower Edmonton (p.222) also show square buildings, of otherwise unknown purpose, at the north end of the down platforms opposite the (by 1877) signal boxes, in similar circumstances of track curvature to Bruce Grove, so these may be further instances of 1872 boxes being replaced; however there is no photographic evidence in these cases.

Also seen is the 1903 road bridge.

17. THE PALACE GATES BRANCH

(Seven Sisters) to Palace Gates

Opened 1878, Great Eastern Railway. Closed and lifted (except as noted).

There are no remains of any of the station buildings on this line and in consequence they are not covered in this book.

Current status of trackbed

Seven Sisters to GR 330890	Eliminated
GR 330890 to Avenue Road (GR 328891)	Allotments
Avenue Road to Downhills Park Road (GR 319897)	Eliminated
Downhills Park Road to east of Westbury Avenue (GR 316898)	Allotments
GR 316898 to NW of Station Road (GR 307904)	Eliminated
GR 307904 to NW of Park Avenue (GR 304906)	Intact but inaccessible
GR 304906 to GR 303907 (SE half of Palace Gates station platforms)	Eliminated (new building on site)
Beyond GR 303907 (adjacent to former Palace Gates station footbridge)	Track remains

BRIDGE 1971, overbridge, Avenue Road, GR 328891. 1878, stock brick, segmental arch (four rings), plain parapet walls, curved wing walls.

BRIDGE 1973, overbridge, Cornwall Road, GR 326892. 1878, plate girder, stock brick parapet walls (bricked in).

BRIDGE 1974, West Green Road, GR 325893. Only the parapet wall on the south side of the road remains.

WEST GREEN

[No remains of station].

BRIDGE 1975, overbridge, Belmont Road, GR 322895. 1878, stock brick, two segmental arches (four rings), panelled red brick parapet walling (not original?), curved wing walls.

NOEL PARK

[No remains of station].

[BRIDGE 1983, underbridge, Park Avenue, GR 305905. Only the red brick abutments remain].

PALACE GATES

[No remains of station structures].

20 staff cottages built 1903 in Dorset Road (formerly Ellesborough Road) (12) and Bridge Road (8), contract to A.J. Bateman 3.6.1903 at £4,297 (outturn cost £4,937).

Avenue Road bridge, a recent view.

Belmont Road bridge photographed on the same day.

The 1903 Palace Gates cottages are to a variant not previously featured in these volumes, with segmental-arched windows on both floors, and a wide three-course string course. They are built wholly in white brick. This is the Bridge Road terrace, which remains in largely unaltered condition. It is built on a slope and the changes of height are arranged on a 1/2/2/2/1 basis.

A 1904 pair at Westerfield are the same except for having a second window on the front, and side doors. Other somewhat similar contemporary cottages with the string course are those at Manningtree and Shenfield (*ERH* p.52 / *ERHS* p.86 top).

18. THE SOUTHBURY LOOP

(Bury Street Jn) to (Cheshunt Jn)

Opened 1891, Great Eastern Railway

BRIDGE 1987, underbridge, Lincoln Road, GR 347957. u1891, four main girders serving as railbearers, plate decking, plate parapets. 24ft 10in span.

CHURCHBURY / SOUTHBURY

Main building at road level, covered stairways, and platform canopies 1891. Booking Hall renovated 1985/6. (Photos pp. 248/249/253).

[Southern half of both canopies, and 1891 platform buildings, demolished c.1985; but the red brick rear walls remain at full height].

[1891 Cottages and SM's house demolished c.1990].

BRIDGE 1988, overbridge, station building and Southbury Road. 1891, segmental arch (four rings), faced in engineering brick up to crown of arch, above which is the red brick of the station building. 25ft 5in span. Widened on north side 1911, plate girder, concrete deck, plate parapets.

BRIDGE 1990, overbridge, Tyberry Road, GR 349970. 1891, segmental arch (four rings), brick parapet walls, all faced in engineering brick, 25ft 6in span.

BRIDGE 1991, overbridge, Brick Lane, GR 350972. 1891, segmental arch (four rings), brick parapet walls, all faced in engineering brick, 25ft 6in span.

BRIDGE 1993, overbridge, Carterhatch Lane, GR 350975. 1891, segmental arch (four rings), brick parapet walls, all faced in engineering brick, 25ft 6in span.

BRIDGE 1994, overbridge, Palmers Lane, GR 350978. 1891, plate girder, cross girders and transverse jack arching, engineering brick abutments and parapet walls.

BRIDGE 1995, overbridge, Hoe Lane, GR 350982. 1891, segmental arch (four rings), brick parapet walls, all faced in engineering brick, 25ft 4in span. (Photo p.252).

BRIDGE 1996, underbridge, Longfield Road, GR 351987. Rebuilt 1957, welded steel girders, three main girders, transverse joists in concrete, concrete flooring.

BRIDGE 1997, underbridge, Turkey Street, GR 351988. Rebuilt 1957, welded steel girders, three main girders, transverse joists in concrete, concrete flooring.

BRIDGE 1998, underbridge, Turkey Brook, GR 351988. Segmental arch (five rings), all faced in engineering brick, 34ft 10in span (36ft 8in on skew). (Photos pp. 249/250).

BRIDGE 1998A, side bridge, carries footpath from former down side B.O. (?) building to subway over Turkey Brook alongside Bridge 1998. Segmental arch (five rings), all faced in engineering brick. (Photo p.249).

BRIDGE 1998B, side bridge, carries station approach road over Turkey Brook. Segmental arch (five rings), all faced in engineering brick. Joined to Bridge 1998 by retaining walls for the Brook. 36ft span. (Photo p.249).

FORTY HILL / TURKEY STREET

Replacement Booking Office in viaduct, with canopy, 1988 (canopy extends over subway arch too). New steel stairways within old stair walls 1988. Platform shelters 1988. Former down side Booking Office (?) building, now a shop and greatly altered, 1891. (Photos p.249).

[1891 Main Booking Office building on up side demolished 1988. 1891 platform buildings including the bases, and 1960 canopies, demolished].

[1891 cottages and SM's house demolished c.1990].

BRIDGE 1999, overbridge, Bullsmoor Lane, GR 353998. 1891, segmental arch (four rings), all faced in engineering brick. Widened 1927.

Park Lane Crossing. One pair of cottages, 1891 (Nos 103/105). (Photo p.253).

THEOBALDS GROVE

Whole station is on viaduct, nineteen 4-ring segmental arches, separate higher 3-ring arches for platforms, all faced in engineering brick. Booking Office building 1891, red brick, altered 1978. Subway and covered stairways to platforms 1891. Platform shelters 1990. (Photos pp. 250-252).

[1891 platform buildings demolished but bases remain. 1960 canopies demolished].

[1891 cottages and SM's house demolished 1987/8].

BRIDGE 2003, underbridge, Station Road (the roadway adjacent to the BO building). 1891, segmental arch (five rings), all faced in engineering brick, 30ft span, panelled parapet walls. Contiguous with station viaduct and Bridges 2004/2005. (Photos pp. 250/252).

BRIDGE 2004, underbridge, Crossbrook Street. Plate girder, three main girders, cross girders and transverse jack arching, three spans with two rows of three cast iron columns as intermediate supports, plate parapets, 65ft total span (71ft 6in on skew). Engineering brick abutments. (Photos pp. 250/252).

BRIDGE 2005, side bridge, footway over stream, joists and troughs, engineering brick panelled parapet walls, 12ft span. (South of Bridge 2006).

BRIDGE 2006, underbridge, stream, immediately northeast of Crossbrook Street. Segmental arch (five rings), all faced in engineering brick, 25ft span, panelled parapet walls.

BRIDGE 2007, underbridge, footpath (originally occupation), GR 352013. Segmental arch (four rings), all faced in engineering brick, 15ft span, panelled parapet walls. (Photo p.252).

All three stations had similar platform buildings, a short one on the down side and a longer one on the up side with two cross-gables. They had tile hanging in the gables. The Southbury platform buildings seen here were at ground level, whereas those at Turkey Street and Theobalds Grove were built on arching (photos pp. 249/251). *All these buildings were demolished in the 1980s.*

D.J. Taylor

GER 'standard' canopies were provided on this line, with longitudinal RSJs and timber transverse beams, and the large quarter-circle longitudinal brackets, all as per the New Essex Lines stations (*ERH* p.46 top right). This is the surviving portion of the down platform canopy at Southbury. These canopies retain the original roofing despite the 1985 works here.

A 1977 view of the Southbury canopies when they were still at their fu length. The plain valancing dated from 1960. Turkey Street and Theobald Grove had both lost their canopies altogether by the 1950s, so sho sections of new canopy, using second-hand parts recovered from Stratfor Market, had to be provided for their 1960 reopening, as seen in the photo at p.251 (these however were removed in the 1980s).

D.J. Taylc

Left: Churchbury/Southbury's main building was quite differen from those at the other two stations on the line, because of it overbridge position. The shaped gable is similar in spirit to that a Ilford (1893). This pre-1909 view shows the road side canopy which disappeared during the long closure years. The brackets were of a special design. One wonders what was the purpose of the sma arched opening at left before it was bricked up.

All the buildings on this line were in Ashbee's normal bright re brick, with segmental-arched openings.

J.E. Connor collectior

Below: Southbury in November 1961. A full internal B.O. / Booking Hall modernisation (since altered again in 1985) had been effectec prior to the 1960 reopening of the line, but little exterior alteratior was made. The tall chimneys (a feature at the other two stations also) have, surprisingly, lasted to the present day. The lower section of the building at the far (west) end was removed c.1970.

J.E. Connor collection

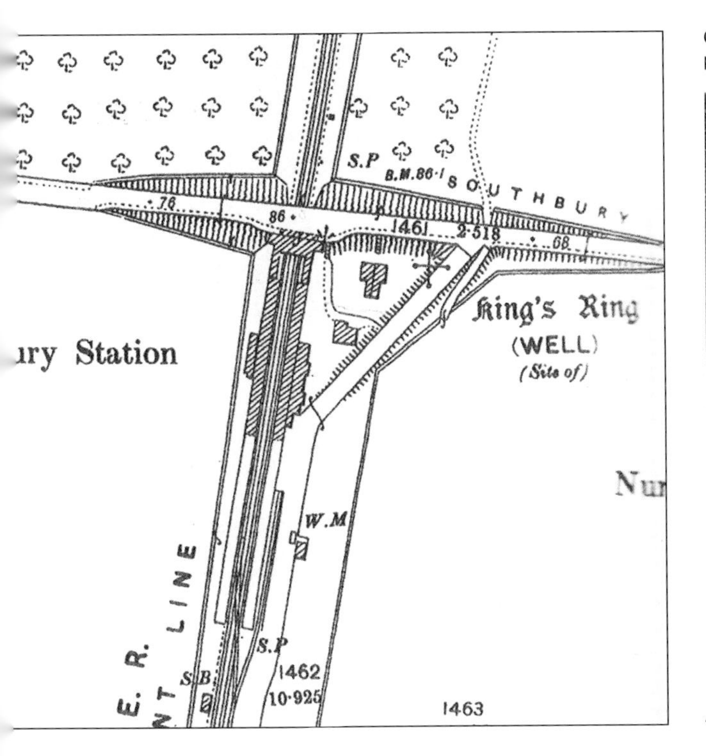

Churchbury 1895 OS. All three stations had a detached Station Master's house and one pair of staff cottages, but none of these survive. Scale 100 yards to the inch.

A closer view of the unusual window design used on the Churchbury/Southbury frontage.

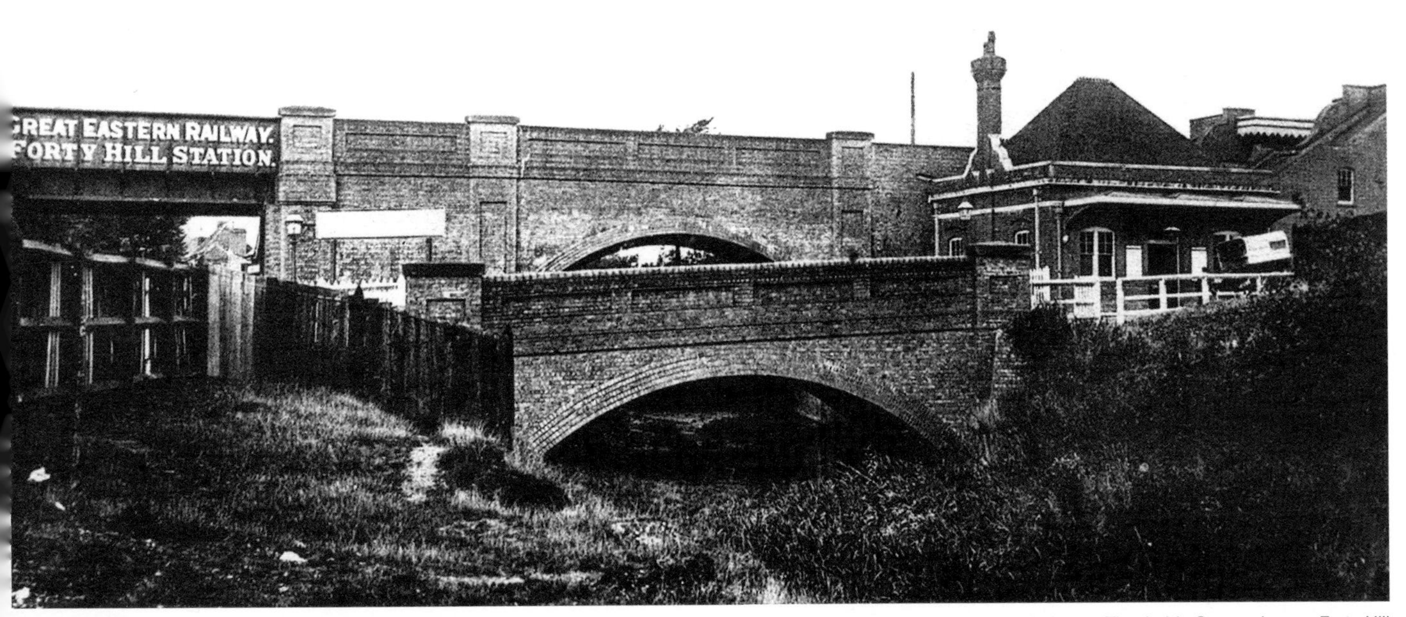

Forty Hill/Turkey Street and Theobalds Grove were arranged on similar lines to each other, although the whole station was on viaduct at Theobalds Grove whereas Forty Hill had the platforms on embankment. The Booking Office buildings at road level were to the same design, with a steeply-pitched hipped roof, and roadside canopies in similar style to Churchbury's.

This 1900s view of Forty Hill is dominated by the bridges. At left is Bridge 1997 over Turkey Street, in its 1891 form. At centre are the two larger bridges over the Turkey Brook, 1998B in the foreground carrying the station approach road and the similar 1998 behind for the railway itself. *P. Laming collection*

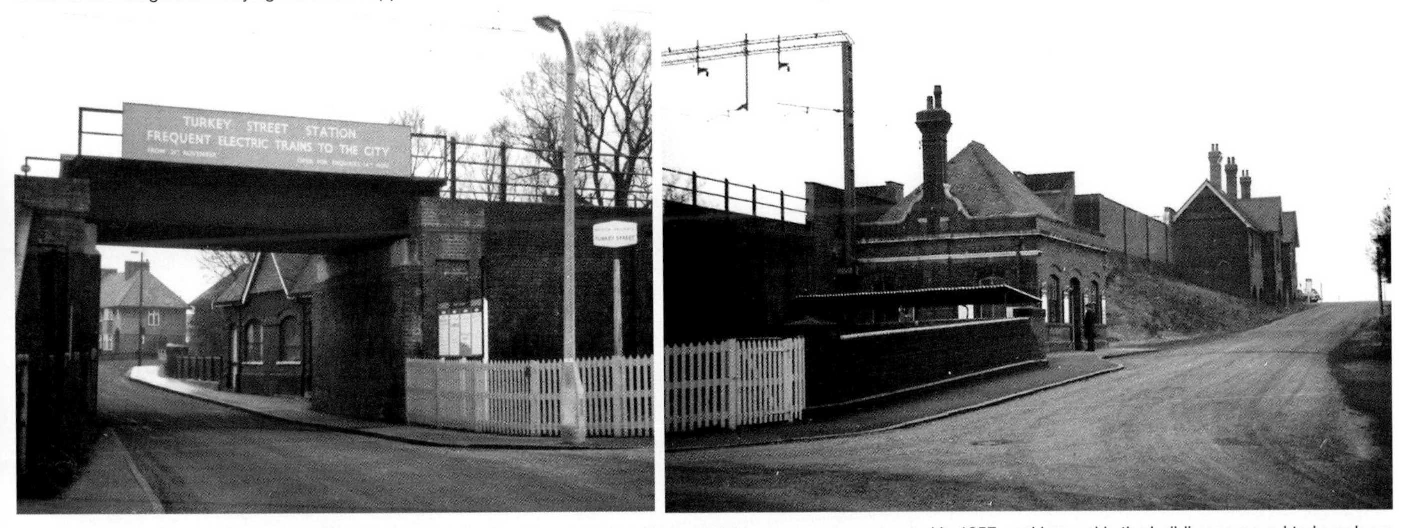

A montage view of Turkey Street in December 1960 shortly after the reopening. Bridge 1997 is seen as reconstructed in 1957, and beyond is the building assumed to have been provided as a down side Booking Office (no actual reference known). It had a roadside canopy originally. By the 1961 plan it was let as a shop, but there is no visible evidence of that in this view. *Nothing now remains of the up side buildings seen here, save for the lower parts of the stairway walls and parts of the platform rear walls.* *Brian Pask*

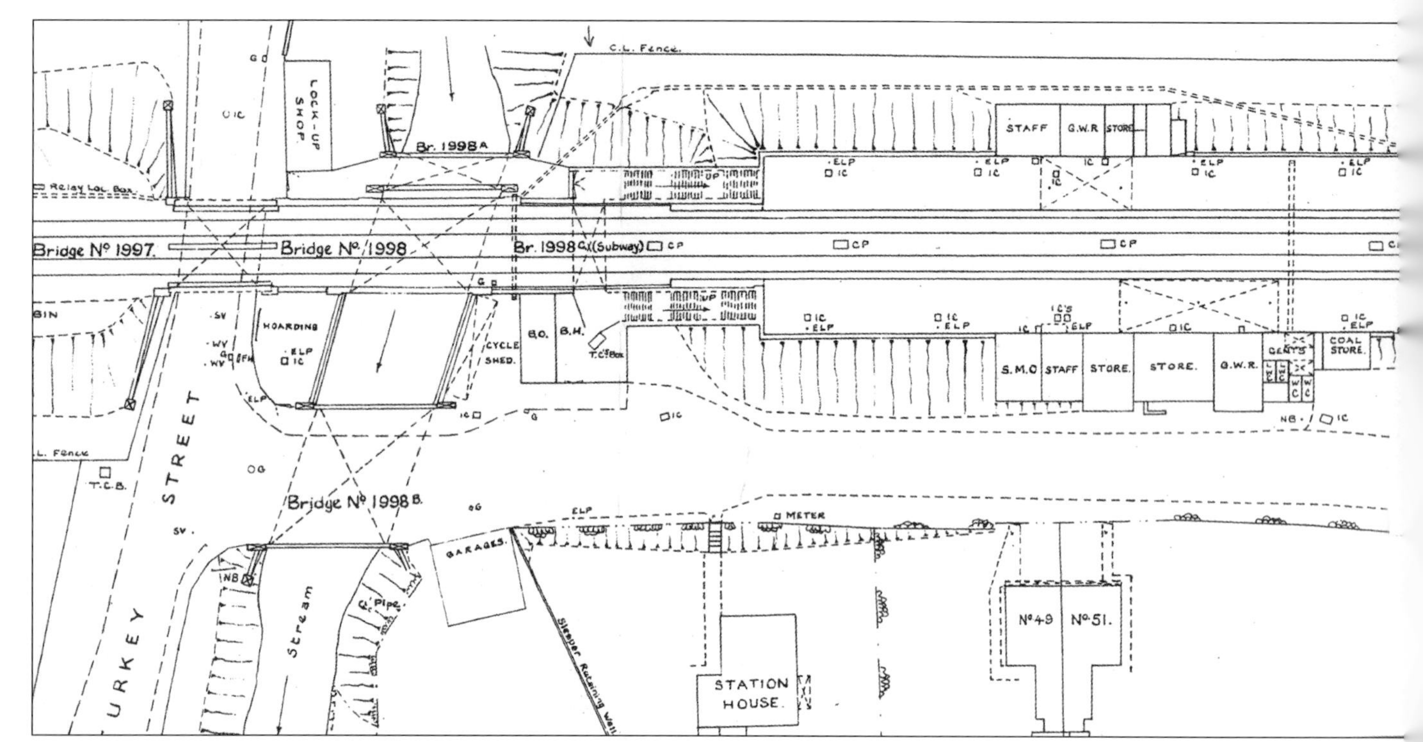

1961 plan of Turkey Street as reopened. The two platform building blocks here were 'handed' the opposite way round to those at Theobalds Grove. Scale 72ft to the inch.

Left: A recent shot of the Turkey Brook Bridge 1998 with the ground level footpath bridge 1998A behind.

Below: Theobalds Grove in the 1900s. The bridges here formed a symmetrical composition. The impression of different coloured brickwork is purely an effect of the light as the same engineering brick was used throughout. The Booking Office building was *not* a mirror-image of Forty Hill, as the entrance doorway was offset to the left. Below the railway stream bridge 2006 at right, the low parapet walls of 'side bridge' 2005 are seen.

P. Laming collection

Theobalds Grove in January 1977, with the station cottages at left. The small entrance canopy to the Booking Hall had been added since 1960. The stairs behind show clearly the divide between the engineering brick facing of the lower parts of the buildings, and the red brick of the upper parts. *D.J. Taylor*

Rear of the up platform buildings on the same day. Although not intended to be seen by anybody of importance, the effect is not very elegant. The engineering brick ends immediately at the crown of the three-ring segmental arches, and there is no relationship between the upper and lower parts. *Since demolished.* *D.J. Taylor*

Two further 1977 views, showing the down (left) and up (right) platform buildings, and the short 1960 canopies erected with columns from Stratford Market. *All now demolished.* *D.J. Taylor*

Left: Exterior view of the west end of the subway, showing the exit door for down passengers (which still exists). *D.J. Taylor*

Above: The Booking Office building shortly after the 1978 alterations. These had involved a completely new, lower, roof, removal of the tall chimney, two new entrance doors and canopy vice two windows, and a new window vice the original door. *D.J. Taylor*

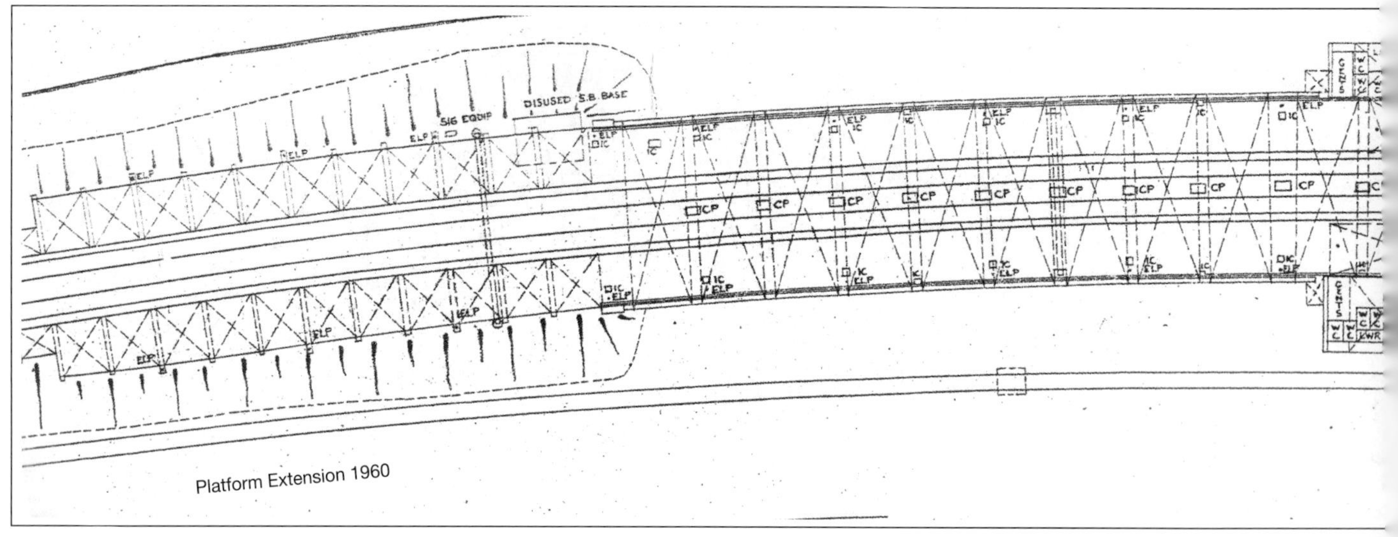

1961 plan of Theobalds Grove. The line was on viaduct from the original south ends of the platforms (by the signal box) to Bridge 2006. Scale 72ft to the inch.

Above and left: Two recent views of Bridge 2004 over Crossbrook Street.

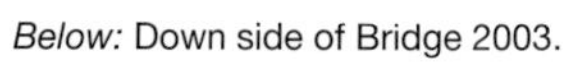

Below: Down side of Bridge 2003.

Left: Hoe Lane illustrates the standard type of brick arch overbridge used on the line, which is as per other contemporary works. These bridges survived the electrification without alteration.

D.J. Taylor

Below: The same design was used for some of the underbridges, as here at Bridge 2007.

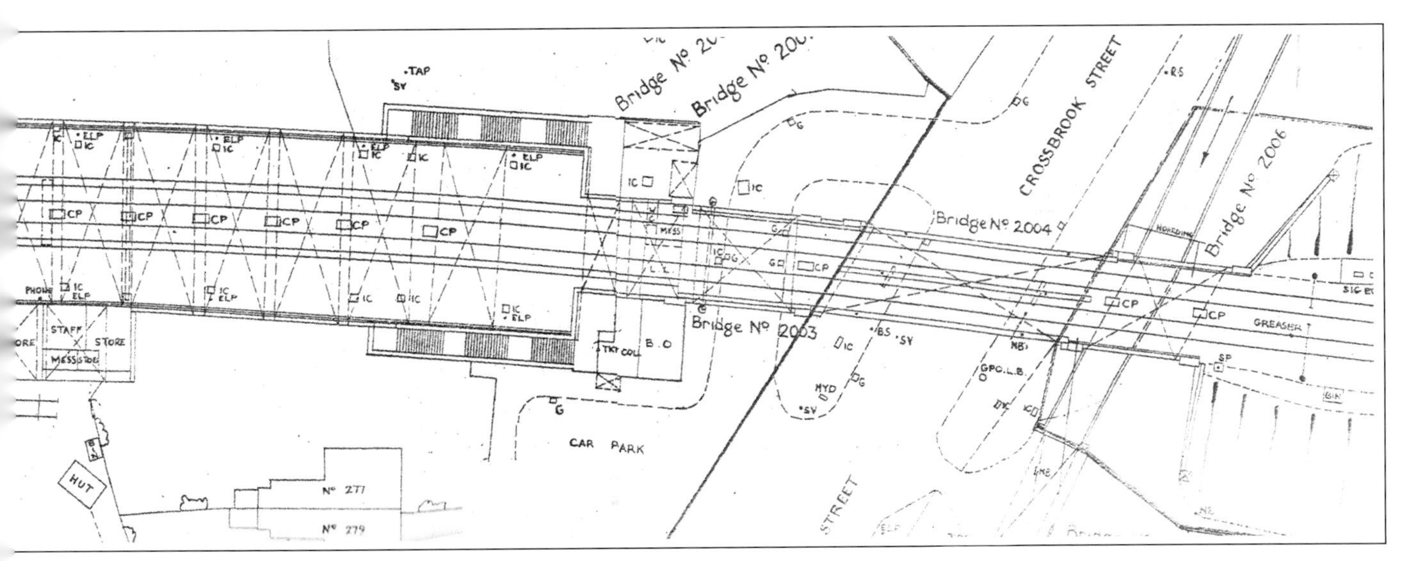

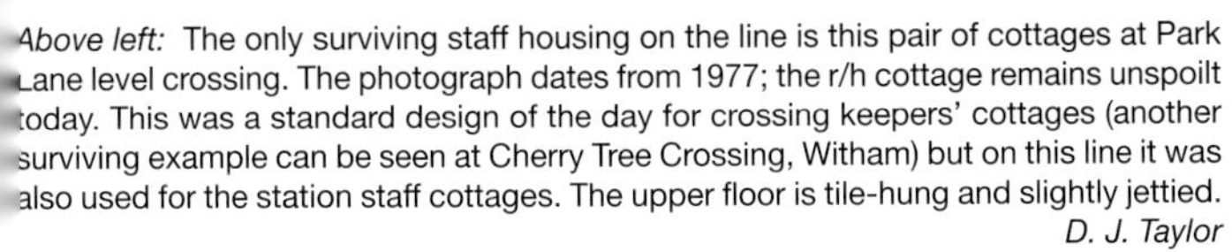

Above left: The only surviving staff housing on the line is this pair of cottages at Park Lane level crossing. The photograph dates from 1977; the r/h cottage remains unspoilt today. This was a standard design of the day for crossing keepers' cottages (another surviving example can be seen at Cherry Tree Crossing, Witham) but on this line it was also used for the station staff cottages. The upper floor is tile-hung and slightly jettied. *D. J. Taylor*

Above right: The Theobalds Grove station cottages. When these were demolished in 1987 it was discovered that they had cavity walls. *D.J. Taylor*

Right: Rear view of the Southbury station cottages, also 1977. The single-storey section housed the scullery. *Now demolished.* *D.J. Taylor*

Below left: The Station Masters' houses *(all now demolished)* were relatively plain, apart from the gable ends. This is Theobalds Grove, 1977. Another SM's house to this design survives at Lowestoft North. *D.J. Taylor*

Below right: The Southbury Station Master's house was already derelict in 1977. *Since demolished.* *D.J. Taylor*

19. THE TOTTENHAM & FOREST GATE RAILWAY

Opened 1894, LT&SR / Midland Joint

For the construction of the line in 1891-4 see *LT&SR* Vol.2 pp. 87-90. The Engineer was Arthur Pain (1844-1937), who had previousl been associated very much with Light Railways, notably the Culm Valley and the Southwold. This line in contrast had very heavy work principally the lengthy sections of viaduct required where it passed through recently built-up (or about to be built-up) areas of terrace housing in Leyton Leytonstone and Forest Gate. A further section through recently-developed housing between Black Horse Road an Walthamstow was built in cutting. There were numerous bridges required for the tight grids of new roads, none of which could be close The overbridges are of minimal interest, but the underbridges included many lengthy skew bridges of some substance (all, of course, quit unknown to those who merely travelled the line by train!). A long-delayed programme of replacing the original underbridges began i 2013. The tabulation here gives the situation as in autumn 2014, but *all* the original bridges are included in the analysis at p.264. Whe Maj. Gen. Hutchinson inspected the line in July 1894, he was moved to comment 'I cannot conclude this report without expressing m opinion of the highly satisfactory manner with which the works of this important railway have been designed and carried out'.

(South Tottenham) to (Woodgrange Park)

None of the station buildings or platform structures remain, and in consequence they are not covered in this book. Detailed illustrated articles on their architecture can be found in *Great Eastern Journal* 156 and 157.

The bridges are all dated '1893' here. There is no actual information as to exactly when each bridge was completed.

Bridges marked * are not described in full detail in this tabulation: see the analysis of the standard types at p.264.

'Railway Cottages', Page Green Road: see p.272.

[BRIDGE 4, underbridge, Midland goods depot line. Filled in 1980s].

BRIDGE 22, underbridge, Markfield Road, GR 342888. 1893, brick arch, 7-ring segmental arch, 42ft span (photo p.262).

BRIDGE 26, stream, GR 343889. 1893, ordinary viaduct arch.

BRIDGE 27/28/29, underbridge, Lea Valley line (Bridge 29 now over Jarrow Road), GR 345891. 1893, plate girder, three spans 55ft 2in / 80ft 4in / 55ft 2in, skew. For details see photos p.270.

BRIDGE 30, underbridge, accommodation, GR 345891 (adjacent to Bridge 29). 1893, 4-ring semicircular arch, 12ft span, (re-?)faced in engineering brick.

BRIDGE 31, underbridge, accommodation, GR 347892. 1893, plate girder, two main girders and longitudinal troughing, stock brick abutments, 12ft span, low.

BRIDGE 32, underbridge, Lea Navigation, GR 348892. 1893, plate girder, 70ft span. For details see photos p.268.

BRIDGE 34, underbridge, road (formerly Tottenham Mill Tail stream), GR 348892. Late C20 welded steel span.

BRIDGE 35, underbridge, River Lea, GR 349892. 1893, plate girder, 73ft 3in span. For details see photo p.268.

BRIDGES 36-47, underbridge, East London Water Works viaduct, GR 349892. New viaduct built 2013 for part length only.

[BRIDGES 48-50, underbridge, Coppermill Stream – filled in 1983 after diversion of stream].

Boundary wall along south side of Forest Road where it runs directly alongside railway from Bridge 50 to Bridge 55; the road was diverted over this stretch. 1893, stock brick, approx 5ft high.

BRIDGE 53, underbridge, Flood Relief Channel, GR 355893. 1959, welded steel girders and cross girders, concrete infill, 59ft span.

BRIDGE 55, underbridge, accommodation, GR 356893. 1958, concreted girders, 40ft span.

BLACKHORSE ROAD (new station).

Platforms, brick shelters and footbridge 1981. LT building 1968.

BLACK HORSE ROAD (old station)

[No remains].

BRIDGE 56, overbridge, Blackhorse Road, GR 359893. c.1990 concrete span, red brick parapet walls, concrete abutments, skew.

* BRIDGE 57, overbridge, Pretoria Avenue, GR 362893. 1893, plate girder, skew.

* BRIDGE 58, overbridge, Stoney Avenue, GR 362893. 1893, plate girder, skew.

* BRIDGE 59, overbridge, Ritchings Avenue, GR 363893. 1893, plate girder, skew.

* BRIDGE 60, overbridge, Suffolk Park Road, GR 363893. 1893, plate girder, skew.

BRIDGE 61, overbridge, Warner Road, GR 364893. c.1960s concrete span, red brick parapet walls, concrete abutments, skew.

* BRIDGE 62, overbridge, Northcote Road, GR 365892. 1893, plate girder, skew.

BRIDGE 63, overbridge, Palmerston Road, GR 367891. New bridge 2014.

* BRIDGE 64, overbridge, High Street, GR 368890. 1893, plate girder, skew. Later bridges for shops on either side.

* BRIDGE 65, overbridge, Vernon Road, GR 368889. 1893, plate girder, skew.

* BRIDGE 66, overbridge, Selborne Road, GR 369889. 1893, plate girder, skew.

BRIDGE 67, Chingford line, overbridge, GR 369889. c.1964, concrete span, skew.

WALTHAMSTOW QUEEN'S ROAD / WALTHAMSTOW

The only old structures remaining are the 1894 footbridge columns (photo p.263) and brick stairs on down platform.

T&FG cottages, Edinburgh Road. Five on NE side, eight on SW side. 1892. (Photo p.271).

BRIDGE 68, overbridge, Shrubland Road, GR 371887. 1893, stock brick, segmental arch, concrete abutments, 29ft span, skew (photo p.263).

BRIDGE 69, overbridge, Albert Road, GR 372887. Late C20 steel girder, skew.

* BRIDGE 70, overbridge, Queen's Road, GR 372886. 1893, plate girder, skew.

* BRIDGE 71, underbridge, Boundary Road, GR 375882. 1893, plate girder, transverse troughing.

* BRIDGE 97, underbridge, Lea Bridge Road, GR 376880. 1893, plate girder (three spans), transverse troughing, skew.

T&FG cottages, Dunton Road. Ten remain of original fourteen. 1892 (photo p.272).

* BRIDGE 117, underbridge, Capworth Street, GR 378878. 1893, plate girder (three spans), transverse troughing.

* BRIDGE 126, underbridge, Beaumont Road, GR 379877. 1893, plate girder (three spans), transverse troughing, skew.

BRIDGE 133, underbridge, Skelton's Lane, GR 379877. 2014, welded steel span.

[* BRIDGE 139, underbridge, Bosanquet's occupation. Filled in 1982].

* BRIDGE 153, underbridge, (Leyton) High Road, GR 381875. 1893, plate girder (three spans), transverse troughing, skew. For details see photos p.267.

LEYTON MIDLAND ROAD / LEYTON

Platforms on viaducts either side of main viaduct (arches 157-173). 1894 down platform brick stairway (roofing removed). Late C20 steel stairs up side, within 1894 stair walls. Arches 154/155/156 have white glazed bricks.

* BRIDGE 175, underbridge, Hainault Road, GR 383874. 1893, plate girder (three spans), transverse troughing, skew.

* BRIDGE 207, underbridge, Grove Green Road, GR 389872. 1893, plate girder, transverse troughing.

BRIDGE 233, underbridge, Ongar line (GER Bridge 674A), GR 391870. 1893, plate girder, three main girders, no parapets, 50ft 6in span, skew. New red brick abutments either end 1990s in connection with the additional bridge over the M11 extension immediately to west.

LEYTONSTONE HIGH ROAD / LEYTONSTONE

Up platform on viaduct alongside main viaduct (the main viaduct is abnormally wide to carry the down platform and the goods sidings). 1894 down platform stairway, faced with white glazed brick (roofing removed). 1894 up platform stairway (roofing removed 1940). Arches 258-263 have white glazed bricks. [1957 platform buildings removed 1996].

* BRIDGE 264, underbridge, Leytonstone High Road, GR 394868. 1893, plate girder (three spans), transverse troughing, skew.

* BRIDGE 274, underbridge, Lancaster Road, GR 395867. 1893, plate girder (three spans), transverse troughing, skew.

BRIDGE 283, underbridge, Lansdowne Road, GR 395866. New single-span welded girder bridge on new concrete abutments 2013, skew.

BRIDGE 289, underbridge, Sansom Road, GR 395866. New single-span welded girder bridge on new concrete abutments 2013, skew.

BRIDGE 296, underbridge, Acacia Road (formerly Forest Road), GR 395865. New single-span welded girder bridge on new concrete abutments 2013, skew.

BRIDGE 302, underbridge, Montague Road, GR 395865. New single-span welded girder bridge on new concrete abutments 2013, skew.

BRIDGE 304, underbridge, Harrow Road, GR 397864. New single-span welded girder bridge on new concrete abutments 2013, skew.

* BRIDGE 311, underbridge, Courtenay Road (originally occupation), GR 397864. 1893, plate girder, transverse troughing.

[BRIDGE 319, underbridge, accommodation - filled in].

[BRIDGE 323, underbridge, Cobbold Road – bricked up 1983].

* BRIDGE 331, underbridge, Cannhall Road, GR 399862. 1893, plate girder (three spans), transverse troughing, skew.

* BRIDGE 337, underbridge, Ramsay Road, GR 399862. 1893, plate girder (three spans), transverse troughing, skew.

BRIDGE 347, underbridge, Thorpe Road, GR 400861. 2013, welded steel span.

BRIDGE 358, underbridge, Pevensey Road, GR 401860. 2013, welded steel span.

BRIDGE 363, underbridge, Vansittart Road, GR 401859. 2013, welded steel span.

* BRIDGE 369, underbridge, Talbot Road, GR 402858. 1893, plate girder (three spans), transverse troughing.

T&FG cottage, Talbot Road, two on NW side (out of original four). 1892.

* BRIDGE 380, underbridge, Strode Road, GR 403858. 1893, plate girder, three main girders, joists.

* BRIDGE 387, underbridge, Bignold Road, GR 403857. 1893, plate girder, two main girders, joists.

* BRIDGE 395, underbridge, Clinton Road (formerly Cobbold Road), GR 404857. 1893, plate girder, two main girders, joists.

* BRIDGE 404, underbridge, Stracey Road, GR 405856. 1893, plate girder, two main girders, joists.

* BRIDGE 408, underbridge, Woodgrange Road, GR 405856. 1893, plate girder, transverse troughing.

WANSTEAD PARK

Platforms on viaducts either side of main viaduct (Arches 409-422). c.1998 steel stairs to both platforms. Arches 413 and 414 have white glazed bricks.

T&FG cottages, Chestnut Avenue, eight on south side. 1892.

BRIDGE 423, underbridge, Avenue Road, GR 406856. 1983, welded steel WR type box girder, steel tray decking.

T&FG cottage, Cranmer Road, one on west side, 1892.

* BRIDGE 440, underbridge, Cranmer Road, GR 408856. 1893, plate girder, three main girders, joists.

* BRIDGE 448, underbridge, Latimer Road, GR 409856. 1893, plate girder, three main girders, joists.

* BRIDGE 456, underbridge, Lorne Road, GR 410856. 1893, plate girder, three main girders, joists.

T&FG cottage, Lorne Road, one on east side, 1892 (photo p.271).

BRIDGE 461/462, underbridge, Sebert Road and Balmoral Road (formerly Tilney Road), GR 402856. 1893, special design, see photos p.269 for details.

[BRIDGE 467 over Shenfield line – see Bridge 71 at *LRH* Vol.2 p.121].

THE VIADUCTS

There are three sections of brick arch viaduct, all still in situ save for Arches 230-232 having been removed for the M11 in the 1990s:

- At Tottenham, Arches 1-26, 300 yards (4 was a girder bridge so there are actually 25 arches). It was originally intended to continue this viaduct further east to the Lea Valley line bridge, but this was changed to embankment.

- Boundary Road to Hainault Road, Arches 72-174 (but six are girder bridges so there are actually 97 arches). Approx. 1240 yards.

- East end of Leyton goods yard to GER Colchester line bridge, arches 176-466, but thirty are girder bridges so there are actually 261 arches). Approx. 3680 yards.

The total number of arches was 383 (now 380).

It was originally planned that the section from Hainault Ro past Leyton goods yard would also be on viaduct, making single viaduct section over three miles long, but it was chang to enmbankment.

The 'East London Waterworks viaduct' (36-47) was not a bri arch viaduct but a sequence of girder spans on brick piers.

Pain had suggested in December 1890 that the viaducts shou be built in concrete, a very radical proposal for the date. Howev the conservative Midland rejected this. Pain was allowed to u

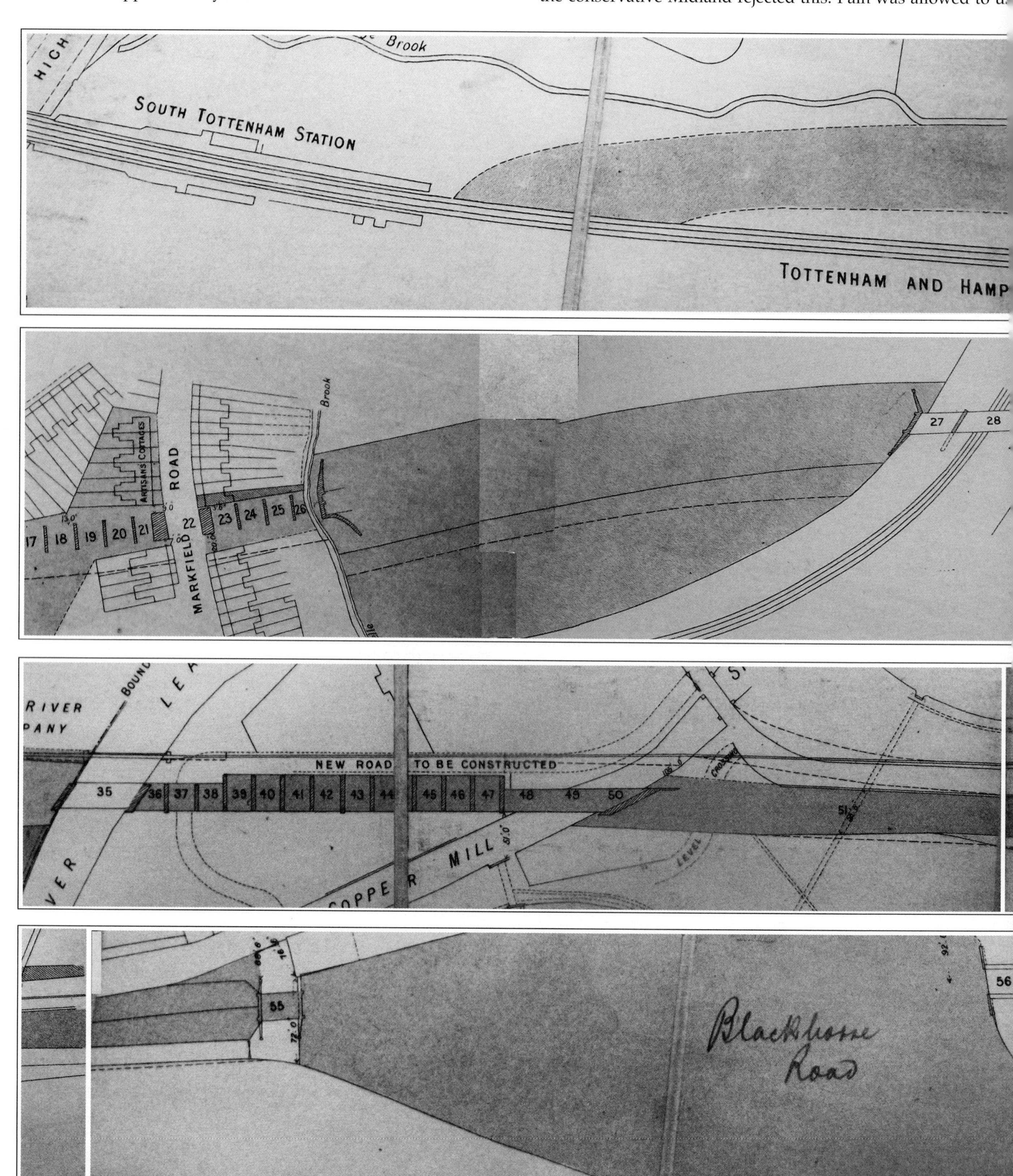

ncrete for the overbridge abutments and cutting retaining walls er the Black Horse Road - Walthamstow section.

As as per the GER viaducts, girder bridges within the brick aducts were given an 'arch number'. On the T&FG, however, ere was no separate system of bridge numbering, so the arch ımbers *were* the bridge numbers, and still are today.

ESCRIPTION OF THE VIADUCTS

Stock brick, English bond. 5-ring segmental arches. 3-course epping out immediately above the head of the arches, with anelled' parapet walling. Mostly 30ft span arches.

The following arches are of shorter (15ft - 20ft) span because of bridges being adjacent: 221, 96, 132, 173, 295, 300, 321, 336, 346, 370, 397, 406, 407, 424, 441.

The following are small 15ft - 20ft span part-width arches in the abutments of skew bridges: 3, 5, 174, 282, 284, 288, 290, 297, 301, 303, 318, 320, 322, 324, 381, 388, 394, 396, 403, 405.

Several 'strengthening arches' half way along long runs were given longitudinal buttresses: 84, 107, 186, 194, 432.

The viaducts carrying the platforms (contiguous with the main viaduct) at Leyton Leytonstone and Wanstead Park have higher 4-ring segmental arches.

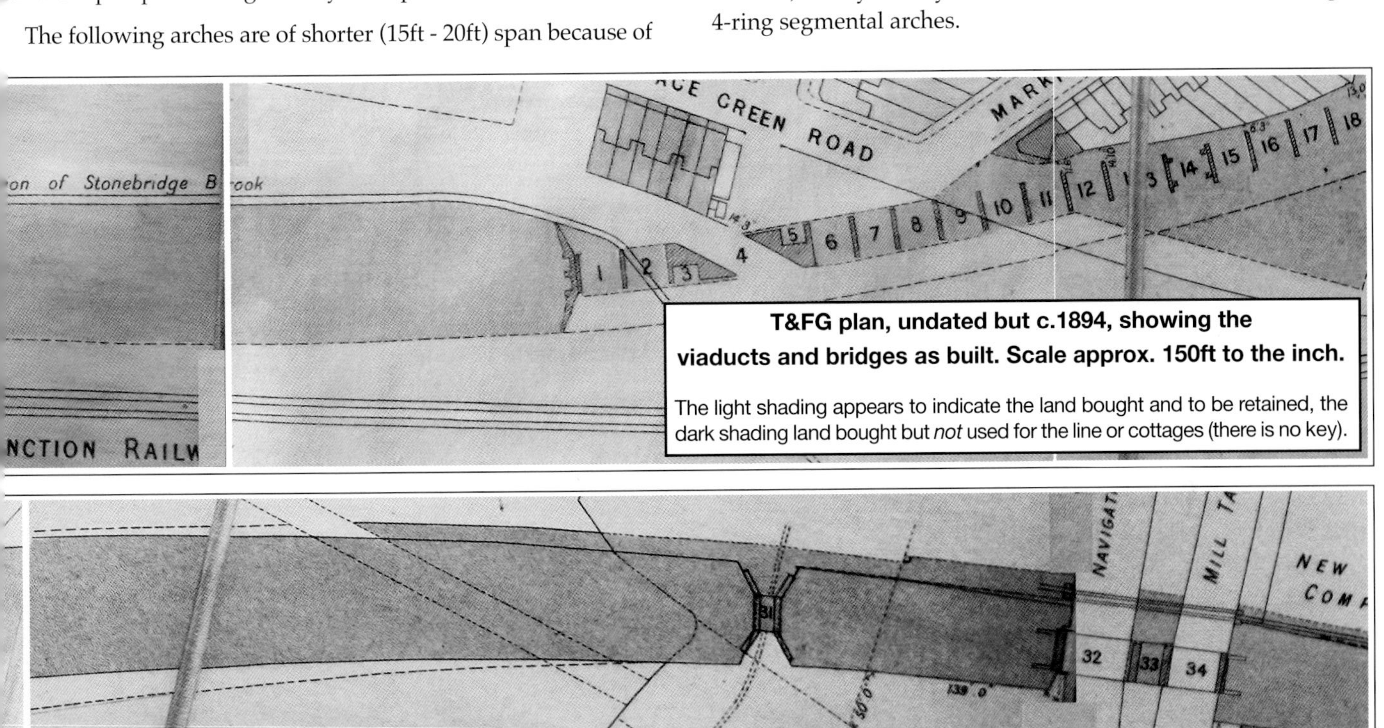

T&FG plan, undated but c.1894, showing the viaducts and bridges as built. Scale approx. 150ft to the inch.

The light shading appears to indicate the land bought and to be retained, the dark shading land bought but *not* used for the line or cottages (there is no key).

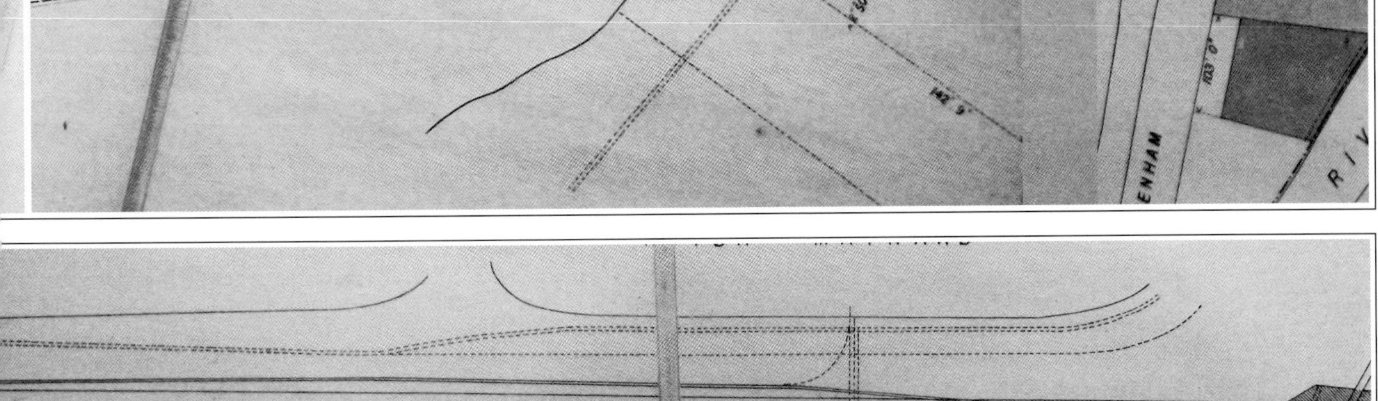

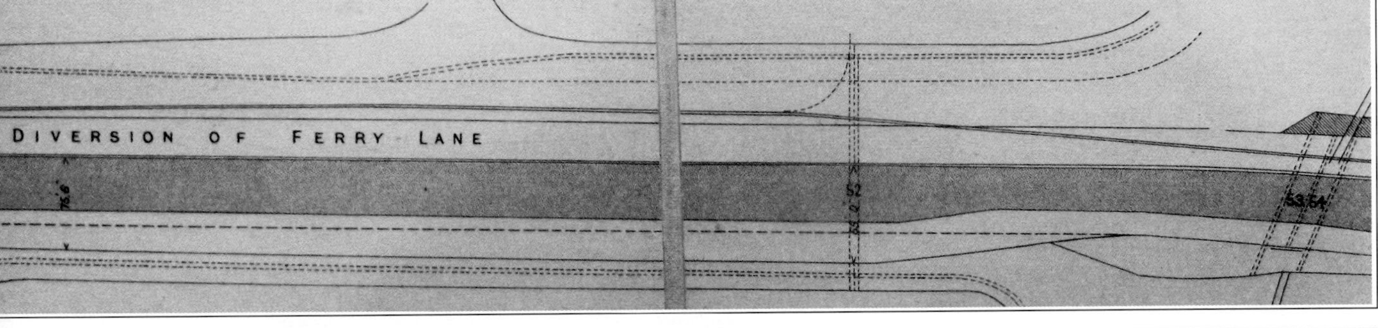

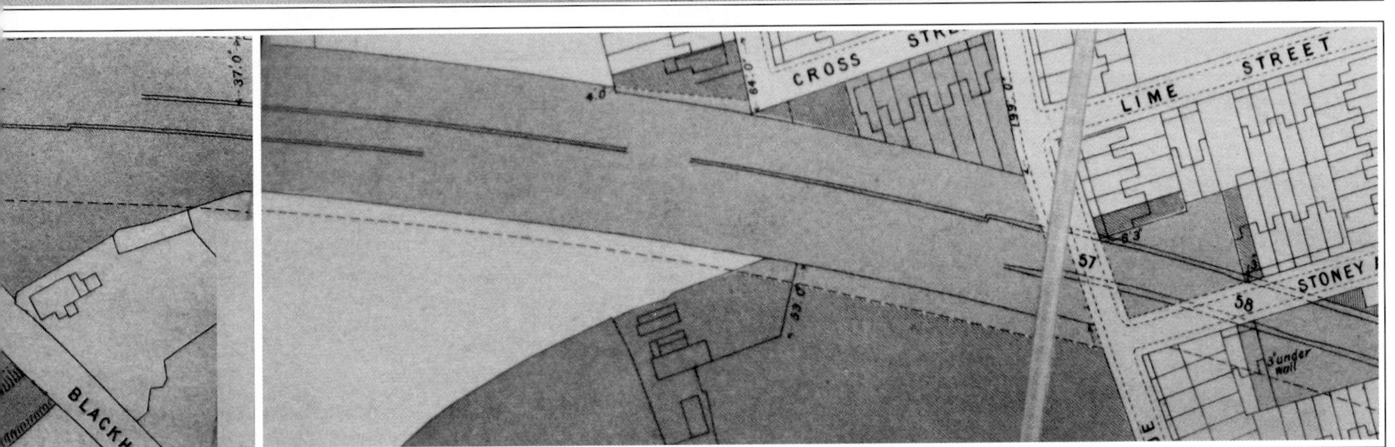

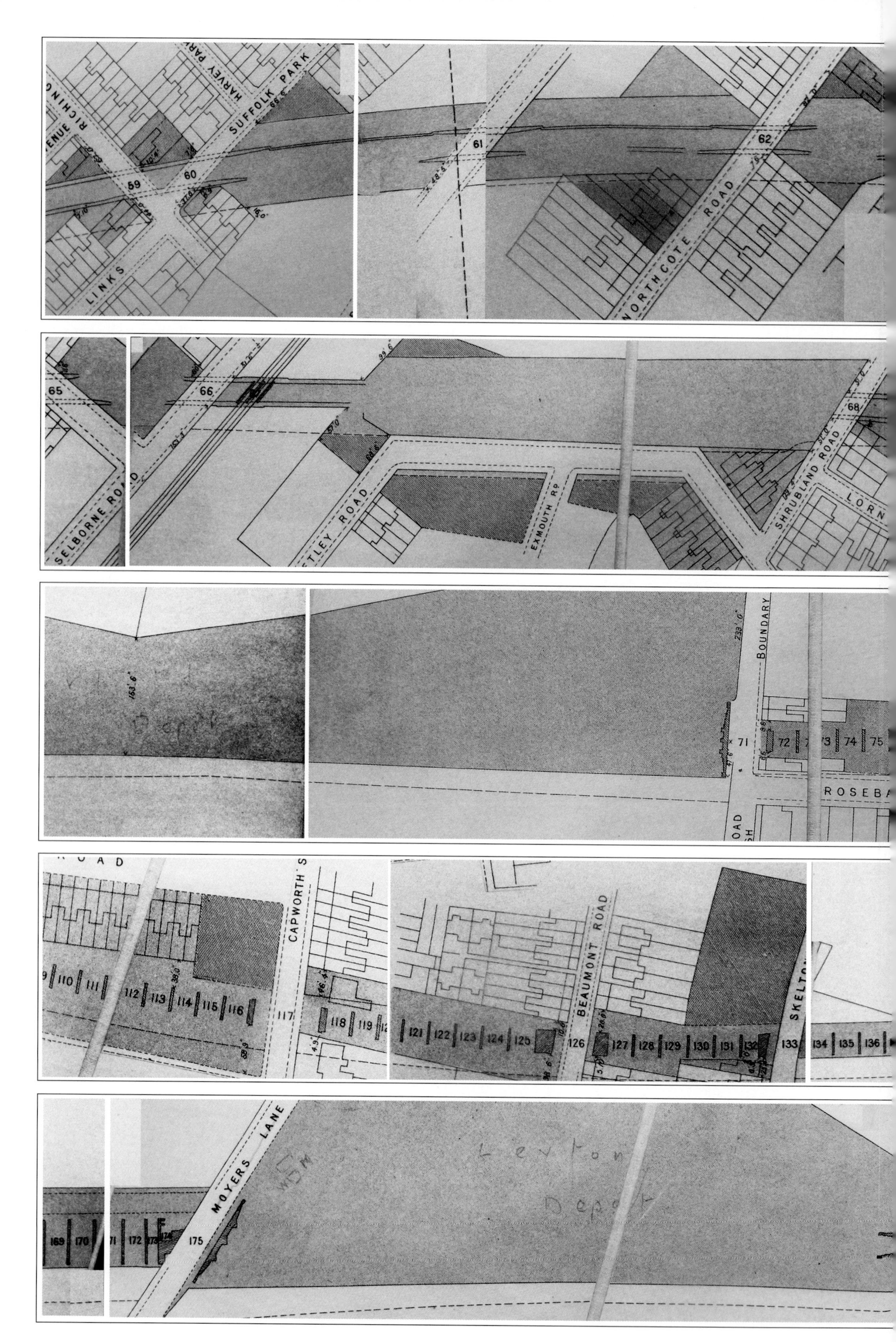

RICHMOND
AVENUE
HARVEY PARK
SUFFOLK PARK
LINKS
59
60
61
62
NORTHCOTE ROAD
65
66
68
SELBORNE ROAD
EXMOUTH RD
SHRUBLAND ROAD
LORN
BOUNDARY
ROAD
71
72
73
74
75
ROSEBA
CAPWORTH S
BEAUMONT ROAD
SKELTO
110
111
112
113
114
115
116
117
118
119
121
122
123
124
125
126
127
128
129
130
131
132
133
134
135
136
MOYERS LANE
169
170
172
173
174
175
Leyton Depot

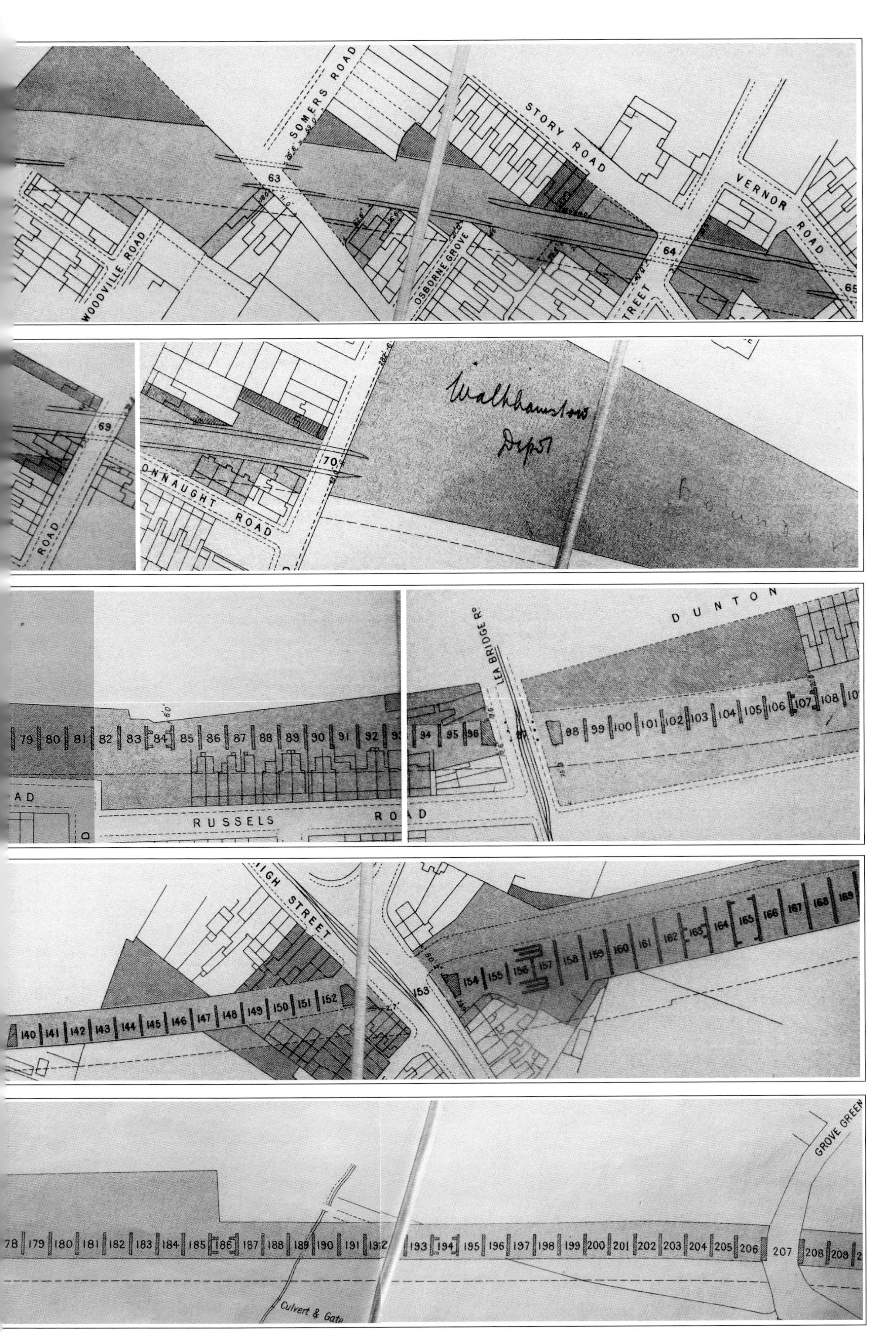
SOMERS ROAD
STORY ROAD
VERNOR ROAD
WOODVILLE ROAD
OSBORNE GROVE
STREET
63
64
65
69
70
ROAD
ONNAUGHT ROAD
Walthamstow Depot
DUNTON
LEA BRIDGE Rd
RUSSELS ROAD
AD
79 80 81 82 83 84 85 86 87 88 89 90 91 92 93 94 95 96 97 98 99 100 101 102 103 104 105 106 107 108
HIGH STREET
140 141 142 143 144 145 146 147 148 149 150 151 152 153 154 155 156 157 158 159 160 161 162 163 164 165 166 167 168 169
GROVE GREEN
179 180 181 182 183 184 185 186 187 188 189 190 191 193 194 195 196 197 198 199 200 201 202 203 204 205 206 207 208 209
Culvert & Gate

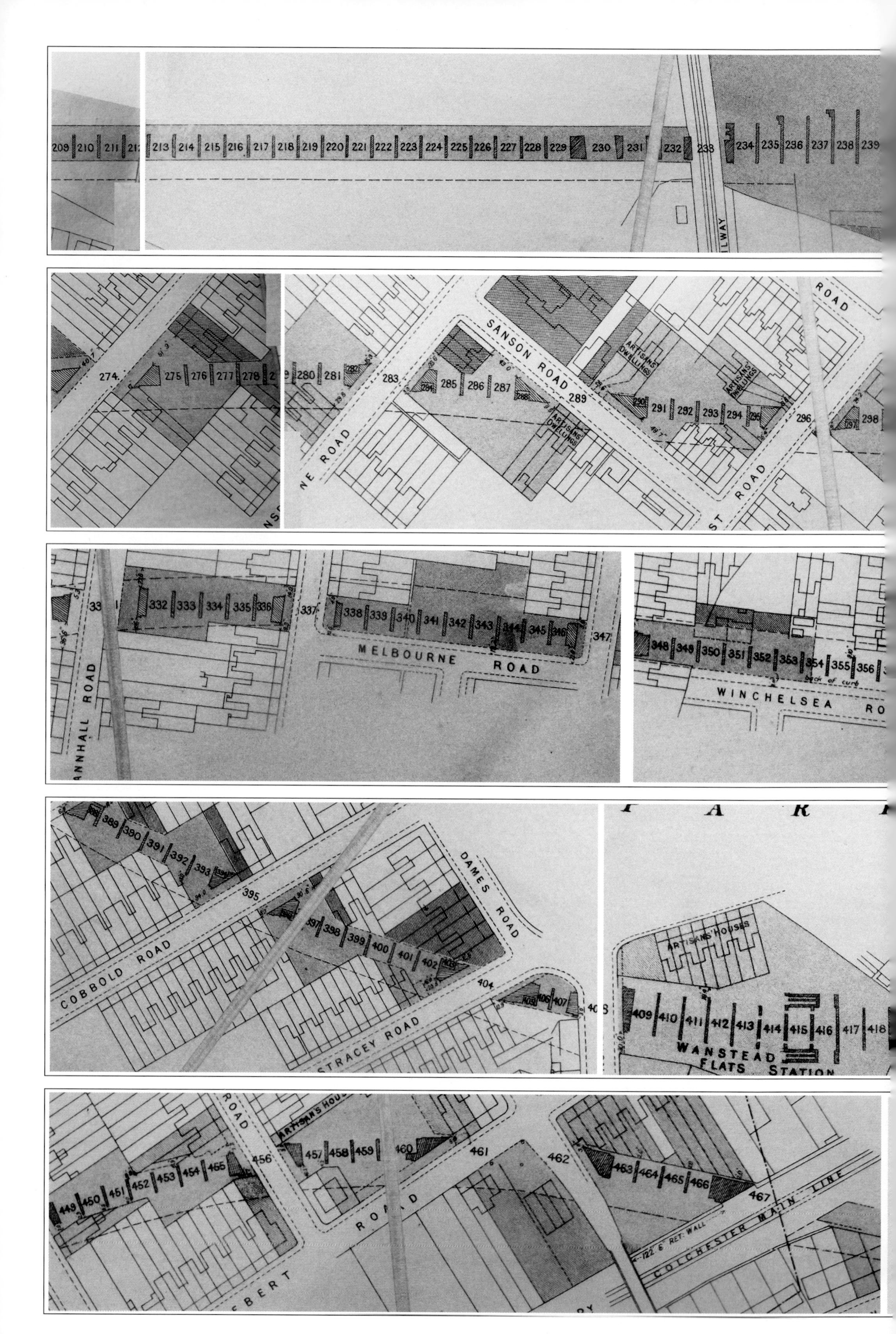

SANSON ROAD
ARTISANS' DWELLINGS
MELBOURNE ROAD
WINCHELSEA
COBBOLD ROAD
DAMES ROAD
STRACEY ROAD
ARTISANS' HOUSES
WANSTEAD FLATS STATION
COLCHESTER MAIN LINE

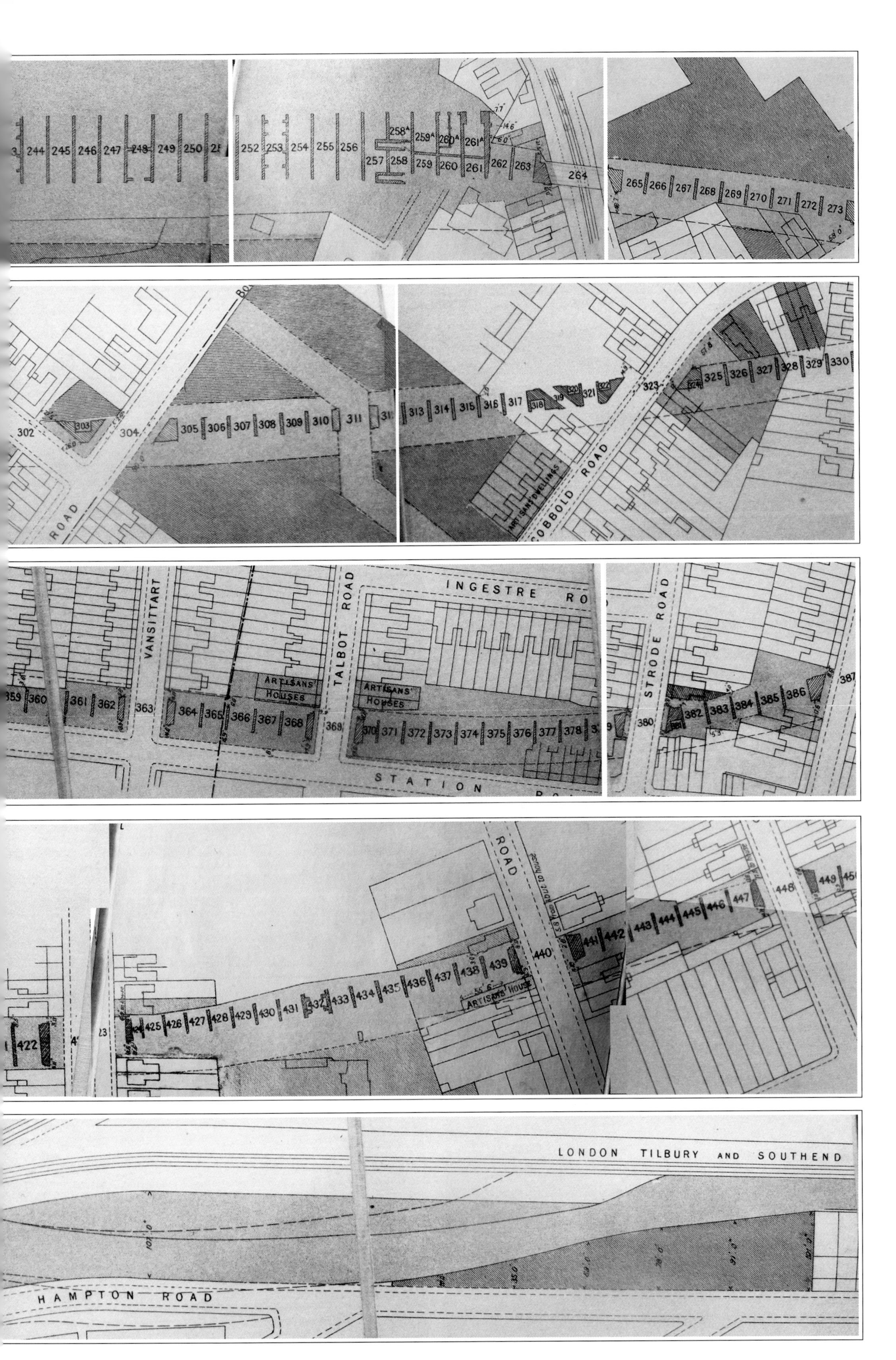
ARTISANS' DWELLINGS
COBBOLD ROAD
VANSITTART
TALBOT ROAD
INGESTRE RO
ARTISANS' HOUSES
STRODE ROAD
STATION
ROAD
ARTISANS' HOUSE
LONDON TILBURY AND SOUTHEND
HAMPTON ROAD

Above
Nowhere in the T&FG viaducts is there any section with open arches to provide an attractive view. Here we look west along the south side from Arch 427 east of Avenue Road, along one of the access roadways provided for tenants.

Above right
Arch 229 remains open. This is the lowest portion of the viaduct. There is a whole run of arches westward from 229 where there is no 'panelling' in the parapet wall (and no signs of anything having been altered). At right, where the Dyers Hall girder bridge was previously, is a glimpse of the red brick western abutment of the M11 bridge.

Right
The short section between Stracey Road (bridge at left) and Woodgrange Road has recently been cleaned and shows how even a plain viaduct like this can be an attractive feature if in good condition. The three stepped out courses above the arches show up well here. There are also two stepped out courses at the head of the parapet wall 'panels'. Arches 406 and 407 seen here are both of non-standard short span (15ft / 20ft) because of their location between two bridges. The filled-in 15ft Arch 405 at far left is one of the part-width arches in skew bridge abutments.

Above left
Markfield Road (Bridge 22) is the only brick arch *road* underbridge on the T&FG. It has a 42ft span and in consequence a 7-ring arch. The parapet wall has been cut down. Of the other brick arch underbridges, 26 is just an ordinary viaduct arch with a stream passing through, and 30 is (and 33 was) small 12ft occupation arches adjacent to girder bridges.

Above
Both platforms at Leyton and Wanstead Park, and the up platform at Leytonstone, are carried on higher viaducts contiguous with the main viaduct, with 4-ring segmental arches. This is the down side at Leyton, facing Midland Road. The Leyton and Leytonstone platforms are 17 arches long, those at Wanstead Park are only 14 arches long as they were kept within the space between the Woodgrange Road and Avenue Road bridges.

Left
At the three viaduct stations, the arches used for the station facilities (Booking Office / Hall, SM's Office, parcels, passenger subways) were faced throughout in white glazed brick, this including the exterior face of the arch itself (but not the whole exterior). This is Wanstead Park up side, where two arches, 413 and 414, were used for station purposes. They were situated below the platforms so the exterior was formed by the 4-ring arches carrying the platforms. These two arches are now tenanted as the station entrance has been moved to the road bridge. The section of non-panelled parapet wall above them dates from 1970 when the platform buildings were demolished.

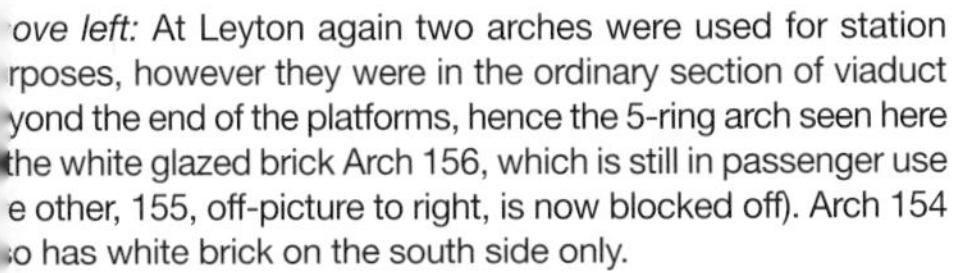
ove left: At Leyton again two arches were used for station rposes, however they were in the ordinary section of viaduct yond the end of the platforms, hence the 5-ring arch seen here the white glazed brick Arch 156, which is still in passenger use e other, 155, off-picture to right, is now blocked off). Arch 154 so has white brick on the south side only.

ove right: At Leytonstone there were six arches with white azed brick, all in the ordinary section of viaduct between the st end of the platforms and the High Road. Only on the up de seen here was there white brick on the exterior. The three rthest arches 258/259/260 by the foot of the stairs were ed for station purposes, the nearer arches 261/262/263 ere always leased for retail use. They were no doubt given is special treatment to encourage more upmarket tenants ecause of their position on the passenger approach road.

ght: Leytonstone remains the best example of the white glazed ick finishing as Arch 258 still forms the passenger route to the own platform, and the down side stairs (seen here) were also ven this finish and retain it today. Unlike all the other stairways, ey were *within* the viaduct not outside it, as the main viaduct rough the station is of extra width through the station to carry e down platform and the goods sidings.

ar right: The sole surviving ironwork structures at any T&FG ation are the footbridge columns at Walthamstow. They have andyside & Co markings.

T&FG OVERBRIDGES

Left: There were only two brick arch overbridges, 59 Shrubland Rd and 60 Albert Rd (now replaced); both stock brick with a four ring segmental arch. The concrete construction of the abutments is evident in this view of Shrubland Rd.

Bottom left: The twelve 1893 plate girder road overbridges (of which nine remain) are of no great interest. This is Bridge 63 Palmerston Rd. As the spans are all short the girders are of minimal depth and the parapet plates of considerable depth (1ft 9in and 6ft 3in here). Again note the concrete abutments, and concrete retaining wall beyond. At Bridges 58, 60 and 65 the parapet plates extend down covering over the girders.

PLATE GIRDER OVERBRIDGES

Plate girder: cross girders, concrete filling, plate parapets, concrete abutments. Of steel construction.

No.	Bridge	Span	No.	Bridge	Span
56	Black Horse Road *	25ft 3in	62	Northcote Road	31ft 6in
57	Pretoria Avenue	48ft 6in	63	Palmerston Road *	37ft 9in
58	Stoney Avenue	48ft 6in	64	High Street	26ft 7in
59	Richings Avenue	30ft 2in	65	Vernon Road	39ft 8in
60	Suffolk Park Road	38ft 3in	66	Selborne Road	32ft 0in
61	Warner Road *	35ft 0in	70	Queen's Road	25ft 7in

Most are on a considerable skew: the *skew* spans are given.

* *1893 bridge now replaced*

Also Bridge 67, Chingford line (photo p.270): this was of a different type and has also since been replaced.

T&FG PLATE GIRDER UNDERBRIDGES

All T&FG girder bridges were of steel (which again was in the forefront of progress for a decision made in 1890/1), not wrought iron.

All the original bridges are listed in this tabulation. Where the original bridge no longer existed in 2014, this is noted *.

Apart from the truss bridge over the Colchester line, the underbridges were plate girder, with plate parapets. Except for those shown separately at end, they were of four standard types as listed here.

The skew figures given here (from the 1894 documentation for the Board of Trade) are in the usual manner by comparison with the line, e.g. 78 deg skew = 12 degrees from straight; the lower the number the greater the skew. Span lengths are from the LMS bridge records.

1 Plate girder, three main girders, transverse troughing, single span

No.	Bridge	Span	Skew
4	Midland goods depot *	span 26ft 0in (47ft 6in on skew)	33 degree skew
34	Tottenham Mill Tail *	span 40ft 0in	straight
55	occupation *	span 40ft 0in	straight
71	Boundary Road	span 48ft 0in	88 degree skew
139	occupation (Bosanquets) *	span 39ft 6in (41ft 2in on skew)	76 degree skew
207	Grove Green Road	span 40ft 0in	straight
230	Dyers Hall Road	span 40ft 0in (40ft 4in on skew)	82 degree skew
311	Courtenay Road (originally occupation)	span 40ft 0in	straight
319	occupation (Nevilles) *	span 12ft 0in (18ft 7in on skew)	45 degree skew
408	Woodgrange Road	span 45ft 0in (46ft 3in on skew)	76 degree skew

2 Plate girder, three main girders, transverse troughing, three spans with cast iron columns as intermediate supports
The side spans are mostly of the same length as each other, and the middle span is always longer.

No.	Bridge	Spans on straight	Spans on skew	Total Span **	Skew (degrees)
97	Lea Bridge Road	18ft 6in / 31ft 4in /18ft 6in	19ft 3in / 32ft 9in / 19ft 3in	74ft 6in	73
117	Capworth Street	25ft 0in / 26ft 4in / 25ft 0in	-	80ft 0in	straight
126	Beaumont Road	15ft 0in / 19ft 0in / 15ft 0in	15ft 3in/ 19ft 4in / 15ft 3in	53ft 1in	82
133	Skelton's Lane *	16ft 9in / 24ft 6in /17ft 3in	17ft 1in / 25ft 1in / 17ft 6in	63ft 0in	79
153	Leyton High Road	19ft 2in / 47ft 0in / 21ft 6in	23ft 6in / 58ft 0in+ / 23ft 6in	108ft 7in	61
175	Hainault Road	8ft 2in / 32ft 6in / 7ft 6in	10ft 2in / 39ft 9in /9ft 0in	62ft 9in	56
264	Leytonstone High Road	21ft 0in / 36ft 0in / 21ft 0in	23ft 0in / 39ft 5in / 23ft 0in	89ft 0in	66
274	Lancaster Road	19ft 0in / 25ft 6in / 19ft 0in	26ft 6in / 36ft 3in / 26ft 6in	93ft 0in	45
283	Lansdowne Road *	16ft 0in / 24ft 9in / 16ft 0in	20ft 6in / 32ft 0in / 20ft 6in	88ft 2in	52
289	Sansom Road *	15ft 9in / 26ft 0in / 15ft 9in	28ft 0in / 46ft 4in / 28ft 0in	105ft 4in	35
296	Acacia Road *	16ft 0in / 26ft 0in / 16ft 0in	20ft 3in / 32ft 6in / 20ft 3in	76ft 6in	53
302	Montague Road *	21ft 6in / 24ft 6in / 21ft 6in	34ft 9in / 40ft 10in / 34ft 9in	114ft 0in	38
304	Harrow Road *	16ft 0in / 30ft 9in / 16ft 0in	20ft 4in / 39ft 4in / 20ft 4in	83ft 6in	51
323	Cobbold Road *	20ft 0in / 23ft 0in / 20ft 0in	29ft 0in / 33ft 9in / 29ft 0in	94ft 8in	44
331	Cannhall Road	20ft 0in / 26ft 6in / 20ft 0in	20ft 3in / 26ft 10in / 20ft 3in	70ft 6in	81
337	Ramsay Road	17ft 6in / 25ft 10in /17ft 6in	17ft 7in / 26ft 0in / 17ft 7in	63ft 6in	87
347	Thorpe Road *	15ft 6in / 26ft 0in / 15ft 6in	15ft 7in / 26ft 0in / 15ft 7in	60ft 0in	87
358	Pevensey Road *	13ft 0in / 26ft 0in / 13ft 0in	-	54ft 6in	89
363	Vansittart Road *	13ft 0in / 25ft 0in / 13ft 0in	-	54ft 4in	89

+ the three girders are of differing lengths, 53ft 1in, 56ft 4in and 59ft 7in *** from 1894 MT6 information - full girder lengths*

3 Plate girder, three main girders, cross girders, four longitudinal joists on each side (supported on bottom flange of main girders), steel plate decking

No.	Bridge	Span	Skew
369	Talbot Road	span 54ft 0in	88 degree skew
380	Strode Road	span 53ft 6in (55ft 6in on skew)	73 degree skew
440	Cranmer Road	span 60ft 0in (60ft 3in on skew)	83 degree skew
446	Latimer Road	span 60ft 0in (61ft 6in on skew)	78 degree skew
456	Lorne Road (some differences, see p.268)	span 60ft 0in (66ft 8in on skew)	64 degree skew

Plate girder, two main girders, cross girders, four longitudinal joists on each side set in top of cross girders, steel late decking [It is normal practice in plate girder bridge design to use two main girders for longer spans but three for shorter spans]

387	Bignold Road	span 62ft 0in (71ft 6in on skew)	60 degree skew
395	Clinton Road	span 62ft 0in (78ft 3in on skew)	52 degree skew
404	Stracey Road	span 54ft 0in (80ft 7in on skew)	43 degree skew
423	Avenue Road *	span 70ft 0in	85 degree skew

[for Bridge 461/462 see p.269].

late girder bridges over waterways and railways

7/28/29	Lea Valley line	47ft 6in / 70ft 0in / 47ft 6in (55ft 2in / 80ft 4in / 55ft 2in on skew)	59 degree skew	Similiar to type 4: see photos p.270
32	Lea Navigation	span 70ft 0in	straight	Version of Type 3, see photos p.268
35	River Lea	span 60ft 0in (73ft 3in on skew)	55 degree skew	As Bridge 32, see photo p.268
8/49/50	Copper Mill Stream *	three spans N. side / two spans S. side, C/I cylinders as intermediate supports		Similar to Type 3
233	Ongar line	span 50ft 0in (50ft 6in on skew)	82 degree skew	As Type 1, no parapets (photo p.270)
467	Colchester line	span 75ft (120ft on skew)	38 degree skew	Pratt truss, see Vol.2 p.121

1 The first type of bridge could not be generally adopted for roads in the Leyton Local Board and West Ham Corporation areas – cept that Grove Green Road and Woodgrange Road were so constructed - because of their insistence on longer overall lengths (see low). It was therefore limited to accommodation bridges in those areas and a few bridges elsewhere.

ridge 71, Boundary Road, looking east. The name of this road is derived from the oundary between the parishes of Walthamstow and Leyton running along it, to be recise along the line of the front garden walls of the houses on the south side (right). Vhilst the Walthamstow authorities were satisfied with the north side abutment being mmediately in rear of the pavement, Leyton insisted on their abutment being set ack to the housing line! The girders are 4ft deep (in line with the normal rule of epth being one-tenth of the span), the parapets 3ft 6in.

Bridge 207, Grove Green Road, looking north. It was probably because this was still 'Grove Green Lane', a 'country lane' outside the developed area, at the time of promotion that the Leyton Local Board did not insist on the abutments being set further back as at other bridges. Girders 4ft deep, parapets 4ft.

Jnderview of Bridge 207, showing the simple trough flooring of these bridges and their three-span equivalent (Type 2). This was a common form of construction in the 1890s, as seen previously on the Blackwall ine widening and Colchester line widening.

Left: Bridge 311, Courtenay Road, south side, was to this design because it began life as an occupation bridge only. As in most cases, the brickwork that previously covered the ends of the girders has been removed here, which shows how extra vertical web stiffeners were provided at the ends. Also note that there are no parapet plates at the ends, where the brickwork originally provided protection. 4ft girders, 4ft parapets.

Above: Bridge 408, Woodgrange Road, with the west end of the Wanstead Park station up platform viaduct at right. There is no evident reason why the authorities should have allowed the abutments to be so far forward on this important main road. There were originally pavements on both sides, but after road widening pedestrians walked through the first arches instead. 4ft 3in girders, 4ft parapets.

2 The second type of bridge was simply a three-span version of the first. They are so numerous because the Leyton Local Boa insisted on the bridge abutments in most roads being set back to the front line of the houses. Because most of the roads were also cross at a considerable skew, this resulted in some cases in total lengths well beyond the sensible limits of a single span – although three spa were in fact adopted even for the shorter road bridges in Leyton. (The 1890 Act itself did not *require* the use of three spans anywhere). T Act did provide that all bridges in Leyton should be 'of an ornamental design', and it was presumably agreed subsequently that t columns constituted such as a design, as there was no other 'ornament'. The intermediate octagonal cast iron columns (two rows of thre were mostly placed right on the edge of the pavement kerbs, which has led to them being seen as vulnerable to vehicle strikes, and be a factor in the replacement programme commenced in 2013.

Bridge 337 Ramsay Road, one of the shorter examples (63ft total span). S in original condition save for removal of the brickwork in front of the gir ends. Because the length of even the middle spans in bridges of this type relatively short, the girders are mostly of little depth, and in consequent parapet plates are of considerable depth (2ft 6in and 5ft 6in, in this case).

Ramsay Road has the manufacturer's name A HANDYSIDE & CO LTD / 18 / DERBY & LONDON cast into the base of the columns (not all bridges ha this). They supplied most of the iron and steel bridges for the line.

Left: View underneath at Bridge 175 Hainault Road, showing the transverse troughing and the 'capitals' of th columns. At many bridges the purely-decorative raised upper portion of the 'capitals' has been remove Drainage channels have been added either side of the middle girder but conveniently for the photograph hav been neglected and fallen off!

Above: Several bridges have the unusual feature of the mileage being cast into the columns. This is Capwort Street (3m 1.50 chains).

Above right: Close view of Bridge 117 Capworth Street showing how the vertical web stiffeners of the girder are also used for the cantilevering of the parapet plates. On all types of T&FG bridges every second third or fourt web stiffener is of greater width than the others, highlighted in some cases by the stiffeners being painted different colour to the web (right). This bridge too has 2ft 6in deep girders and 5ft 6in deep parapets.

Bridge 274 Lancaster Road is still in BR grey, and also is one of the few to retain the full brickwork by the girder ends.

Left: In recent years several of these bridges have been repainted into brighter colours with local area names added on the parapet plates. This is Bridge 97 Lea Bridge Road, west side. Note the column at left has lost the whole of its 'capital'.

Below: With the centre span being 48ft, Bridge 289 Sansom Road has a noticeably greater girder web depth, with the parapets being of slightly lesser depth than the girder. It is seen here in summer 2013 with the abutments for the replacement bridge nearing completion.

Montage view: The most impressive ensemble was provided by the adjacent bridges 302 Montague Road (left, in green) and 304 Harrow Road (right, in BR grey). Again the photographs date from summer 2013, but in this case work had only recently begun on the replacements. Montague Road had the longest total length (114ft) of any of the bridges of this type, however this was due to the considerable (35ft 10in) length of the side spans, and the centre span was only 42ft 3in, in consequence of which the girder web depth was less than Sansom Road. Harrow Road had a 41ft centre span so the girder depth was near-identical to Montague Road.

Bridge 153 Leyton High Road has the longest main span (the three main girders are in fact of differing lengths) and it was no doubt for this reason that it was constructed with a different type of intermediate support column (square section) and brackets. It has recently been repainted in blue with the brackets, web stiffeners and parapet supports in white.

The third and fourth types of bridge were the standard designs for the West Ham Corporation area. Like Leyton, West Ham requir
the abutments to be set back to the house fronts, but they had no interest in 'ornament'! - and in consequence all these bridges were sing
span, resulting in some quite considerable span lengths.

3 Bridges of 50-70ft span (Talbot, Strode, Cranmer, Latimer and Lorne Roads), listed above as Ty
3, had three main girders, cross girders, longitudinal joists (four on each side) and steel pla
decking. The joists were supported in the usual way on the bottom flange of the cross girde
Illustrated here are (above) Talbot Road west side, with the adjacent section of viaduct; (left) t
underside of Cranmer Road; and (below) a general view of Latimer Road.

Lorne Road, the longest span bridge of this subtype, has the cross girders supported at a higher level rather than on the bottom flange of the main girders.

4

'Type 4', used for road bridges of 70-80ft span in the West Ham Corporation area (Bignold, Clinton, Stracey and Avenue Roads), features only two main girders, but the cross girders are of considerably greater depth, and the eight joists are fixed at the top of the cross girders, not on the bottom flange.

Below: underside of Cobbold Road.

Left: Bignold Road west side. Note the patching of the web at left, and the much more visually satisfying appearance of bridges that retain the full brickwork in front of the girder ends. 6ft 3in deep girders, 3ft 6in parapets.

Below left: Stracey Road, which has more closely-spaced web stiffeners at the ends for extra strengthening because of the length.

ight: The unique (owing to the great spans) Sebert Road / Balmoral Road Bridge 61/462 is built very skew over a crossroads and has three spans on its south ide but only two on the north, with intermediate cast iron columns (plan p.260). he eastern span seen here is 74ft on the north side and 96ft on the south. The iddle span (south side) at left has a 40ft span. The western span (out of view to eft) is 96ft 6in on both side. The girders themselves are of so great a depth that o parapet plates were required. The cast iron columns are filled with concrete.

Left: Bridge 461/462 has a most unusual construction There are three longitudinal plates supported on the cross girders, and they carry the three subsidiary cross girders between each main cross girder, which support the decking. Here we look west under the western (Sebert Rd) span.

Right: Maker's name on one of the Bridge 461/462 cast iron support columns. As with most new lines, there is no record in the minutes of the different contracts for the works, but this plate does show that Handysides did not get *all* the bridge work on this line .

RAIL OVER RAIL UNDERBRIDGES

Left is the eastern span (29) of the Lea Valley line bridge 27/28/29, which is n used by Jarrow Road. The 80ft 4in centre span and the two 55ft 2in spans eit side are, as usual, constructed in identical form.

Below: The construction is as per 'Type 4' except that there are only four jo (railbearers).

Above: The T&FG bridge over the GER at Leytonston in the 1930s, looking south. At left are Arches 234/235 the first of the wider arches for the T&FG Leytonston goods sidings. Behind the trees at right is the shor portion of viaduct removed in the 1990s for the M11. I the distance is the GER Dyers Hall footbridge, erecte in 1906 and replaced in 1996 by a longer footbridg crossing the motorway also.

The bridge is as per Type 1 but now at least has n parapets.

Alan Simpson collectio

Left: The original T&FG Chingford line Bridge 67 appears in the foreground of this October 1963 'before record shot taken prior to its replacement. The GER protection clauses (s.25 of the 1890 T&FG Act) had required this bridge to be of four tracks width, but i was in the event built for three.

Beyond are Bridge 66 Selborne Road, Bridge 65 Vernon Road (one of those where the parapet plates cover over the girders), the shops bridge on the south side of the High Street, and Bridge 63 Palmerston Road; the start of the T&FG's run of overbridges through Walthamstow.

Note that the retaining wall at right is of brick rather than the usual T&FG concrete, possibly a GER requirement.

D.J. Taylor collection

T&FG COTTAGES

s.28 of the T&FG Act 1890 imposed the usual requirement that the company should agree 'schemes' with the Local Government Board the provision of new dwellings for a specified number of the 'persons belonging to the labouring classes as tenants or lodgers' whose isting houses were to be demolished for the line. The Board did not normally require the number of new houses built to be such as to accommodate *all* those displaced: it took account of how many other houses were readily available to let locally. In this case, 343 operties, mostly very recently built, were demolished for the line, of which 160 were deemed to be inhabited by eligible persons: but ly 70 replacement 'Artisans' Dwellings' were required, because of the very large number of other new houses already under erection sewhere in the area at this time. The 'schemes' were agreed with the Board in February 1892, and the houses were supposed to be ready thin six months of that date. The cottages are all to the same standard design. Some were lost in the war and later, and 35 remain in 2014. BR days some were let to railway staff. The T&FG also retained ownership of a number of pre-existing houses that it had acquired with e land bought for the line but did not need to demolish, and some of these too were being let to BR staff in the 1960s.

	original no.	no. surviving
Markfield Road west side *	6	-
Cross Street south side +	7	-
Edinburgh Road east side +	5	5
Edinburgh Road west side +	8	8
Dunton Road west side +	14	10
Sansom Road east and west sides *	6	-
Acacia Road (Forest Road) north side *	3	-
Cobbold Road north side * +	7	-
Talbot Road north side *	2	2
Talbot Road south side *	2	-
Chestnut Avenue south side * +	8	8
Cranmer Road west side *	1	1
Lorne Road east side *	1	1

* Identified specifically as Artisans' Dwellings on the plans pp. 256-261.

+ Named in T&FG minutes 19.7.1892 as 'ready for occupation next month'.

There is also a terrace of six cottages in Page Green Road with a 'Railway Cottages 1890' datestone, which are shaded as railway property on the plan p.257 upper, however these are to a different design. No other reference to them is known.

The Lorne Road cottage, one of the odd single or pairs of cottages erected on small pieces of land adjacent to road bridges.

Edinburgh Road east side. Apart from the replacement windows these retain a pleasant appearance.

Standard elevat drawing for the 70 T& cottages, from 'Schemes' Walthamstow, Leyt and West H preserved in the Lo Government Bo records.

Below left: Standard p of ground floor - t rooms, plus kitchen a scullery in the re extension, and outsi WC.

Below right: Standa plan of first floor - thr bedrooms, each with fireplace.

Unfortunately the drawings could not flattened for copying.

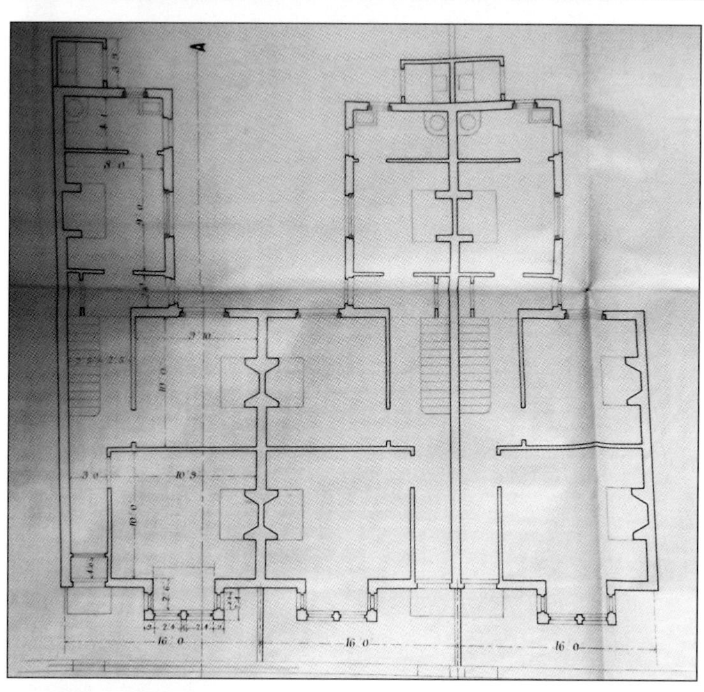

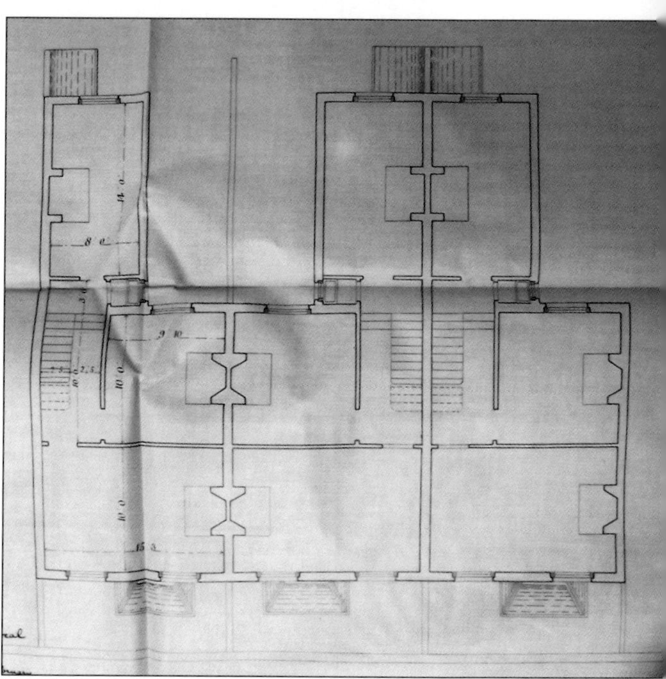

Left: The five remaining cottages at the southeast end of the Dunton Road terrace. The red brick courses used to offset the otherwise stock brick construction show up better here. The two dentillated courses underneath the eaves of the bay windows, and the door and window arches, are also in red brick.

Above: The unexplained Page Green Road 'Railway Cottages'.

▪VHITE TILING AT ▪VANSTEAD PARK

▪/e end our look at ▪e T&FG with two ▪ews of the station ▪rches 413 and 414 ▪ Wanstead Park in ▪eir days of final ▪ecline.

▪ight
Looking south ▪rough the Booking ▪ffice arch 413.

▪elow
From the up side ▪ith the Booking ▪ffice arch 413 at ▪ft.

▪hese arches remain ▪led but are now let ▪ut commercially and ▪accessible.

J.E. Connor collection

FURTHER CORRIGENDA AND ADDENDA TO *LONDON'S RAILWAY HERITAGE* VOLUME ONE

p. 5 bottom Alter to '.....for the DLR in 1985, a 60ft section of railing still in situ west of Three Colt St was removed.....'. Also, the was at this date another section of original railings still in situ on the south side of Arches 349-355.

p.10 The middle right view was taken in 1985.

p.18 Bridge 503 Fast lines: alter to '.....cross girders, joists and plate decking, plate parapets'.

p.24 Bridges 539, 540, 541, 546, 547, 549, 550, 554, and 555 were all taken down in 1985 and rebuilt reusing the old main girders 1986.

p.32 Cantrell Road up side caption. Alter to '.....was most likely done for the NLR line in 1850,.....of the arch brickwork. At left is t southern abutment for the two single-track NLR gasworks sidings girder bridges. When these girder bridges were removed by BR, t new brick parapet wall seen here was provided'.

p.33 Bridge 500 - alter last line to 'of the two single-track girder bridges for the.....'.

p.49 West Ham - the Local lines platform was 1900. Plaistow - the LT substation was opened in July 1960.

p.59 Heathway - the south end of the main building was removed in 1961.

p.73 Bridge 260 - this is 1986.

CORRIGENDA AND ADDENDA TO *LONDON'S RAILWAY HERITAGE* VOLUME TWO

pp.94/95 William St / Blackbird Alley passed through arch 34 (wording mispositioned).

Map p.94 left, text p.95, table p.97 second line, three refs at p.103 bottom, caption p.105 middle Recent research by Richar Bradley on the early development of Shoreditch / Bishopsgate passenger station has shown that the 1847 south side widening was dor as a timber viaduct and that the present brick viaduct widening was done in 1854.

p.96 top map: at left hand end, south side, '1890 Widening South Side' should be shown as commencing at pier 95A/108, and t the left of that should be shown as '1867/8 Widening South Side'. At left hand end, north side, '1871/2 Widening North Side' shoul continue over to p.95 map, commencing at 69.

p.97 Tabulation, re c.1865 north side widening. Alter to '29-43 (all now demolished); all were in line with the 1840 arches. Also bric arch widening of 44 (still in situ)'.

The arch numbering system is pre-1883, as it is used in the 1883 GER Bridge Book; it most likely dates from 1872.

p.125 Between Goodmayes and Bridge 90, add 'GER cottages, south side of High Rd. Terrace of four, c.1892. (Same design as 189 Ongar / 1896 Debden cottages). Much altered'.

p.139 Bridge 739 *does* still exist but it is invisible as it was filled in and the embankment extended around it in the 1960s.

THERE ARE NO LISTED BUILDINGS IN THE AREA COVERED BY THIS VOLUME

And finally a view of the Cambridge Heath street level building of 1894, now removed.

J.E. Connor collection